# Contents

| **Activities** | **Linked to** |
|---|---|

## *Extra*

Extra activities are provided after 23, 31, 39 and 50.

# HOME LINK-UP

Heinemann Educational,
a division of Heinemann Publishers (Oxford) Ltd,
Halley Court, Jordan Hill, Oxford OX2 8EJ

OXFORD  LONDON  EDINBURGH
MADRID  ATHENS  BOLOGNA  PARIS  MELBOURNE
SYDNEY  AUCKLAND  SINGAPORE  TOKYO
IBADAN  NAIROBI  HARARE  GABORONE
PORTSMOUTH NH (USA)

ISBN 0435 03880 X

94 95 96 97 98 10 9 8 7 6 5 4 3 2 1

**Writing Team**
John T Blair
Ian K Clark
Aileen P Duncan
Percy W Farren
Archie MacCallum
John Mackinlay
Myra A Pearson
Dorothy S Simpson
John W Thayers
David K Thomson

Designed and produced by Artistix,
Adwell, Tetsworth, Oxon
Printed in the UK by Athenaeum Press Ltd,
Newcastle-upon-Tyne

# Introduction

Heinemann Mathematics 6 Home Link-up contains 60 homework activities linked to specific pages of the core Textbook and Workbook for this stage of the course.

Teachers can use the activities to provide children with valuable practice at home, related to their work in school. The activities are aimed mainly at consolidating techniques and providing opportunities to apply them. Some activities include problem solving questions. There are also four *Extra* activities, not specifically referenced to the Textbook or Workbook, which provide additional challenges for some children.

For parents, Home Link-up provides
  - the reassurance of a consistent and positive approach to mathematics homework
  - an insight into some of the mathematics carried out in school
  - an opportunity to talk to their children about mathematics
  - a focus for communication with the school.

For children, the activities
  - provide opportunities for individual work
  - help to develop good home study habits
  - encourage responsibility for learning.

The activities are presented as photocopiable sheets. The booklet also includes
  - a contents list
  - advice for teachers about using the materials
  - answers
  - a page of guidance for parents
  - a record sheet.

## USING HOME LINK-UP

### Homework activities

● The activities are intended for children who can benefit from spending more time at home consolidating recently completed or current work in school. They are *not* suitable for children who require further teaching of a topic before they attempt related homework activities.

● Some pages contain two activities, not necessarily of the same length or dealing with the same topics. Other pages contain just one. The underlying principle is that each activity contains work which might take a child 15 to 25 minutes to complete at home.

● The activities are numbered from 1 to 60. A reference to the relevant pages of the Heinemann Mathematics 6 Textbook or Workbook is given in the heading for each activity. For example:

| Heinemann Mathematics 6   Home Link-up<br>Textbook page 22 | Division: by 6 to 10 | **15** |
|---|---|---|

The mathematics contained in each activity is also described in its heading. Activities often cover content related to more than one page of the Textbook or Workbook.

- There are no references to curricular guidelines or teaching notes for the activities in Home Link-up. The appropriate references are those of the core Textbook and Workbook pages to which the activities are linked.

## Special features

- Some activities are intended as expendable worksheets on which children record their answers. These activities are indicated by a pencil symbol.

| Time: 24-hour clock, applications | **49** |

The remaining activities require children to use an exercise book.

- Certain Textbook and Workbook pages carry the symbol **H** to refer to Home Link-up. For example, the reference **H**49 appears on Textbook Page 90 to indicate that homework about that part of the Textbook can be found in activity 49 of Home Link-up.

- Some questions carry a 'Problem solving' flag. For example, this question involving interpretation of 24-hour times appears in activity 49.

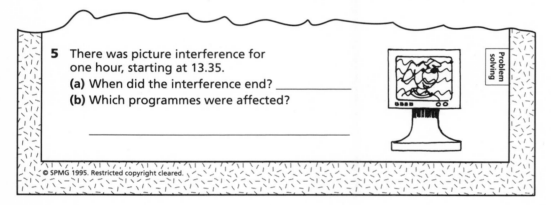

**5** There was picture interference for one hour, starting at 13.35.
  **(a)** When did the interference end? _____
  **(b)** Which programmes were affected?

  _____

Problem solving

© SPMG 1995. Restricted copyright cleared.

-  This symbol is used to indicate homework activities or specific examples where the use of a calculator is recommended.

## Organising and using the children's material

- It is not intended that children tackle all 60 homework activities. A selection should be made to suit their needs and abilities. A typical activity contains several examples. Teachers can select from the examples to suit individual children.

- The contents list in this booklet and the headings of the activities themselves can be consulted when choosing appropriate homework to match work in schools.

- Some of the activities are of a practical nature and are designed to use materials likely to be available at home. Materials required include coloured pencils, a ruler, a calculator, scissors, glue and paper for tracing shapes.

- A photocopied page containing two activities can be cut into two parts before issuing one of them to the children or, if issued as a whole page, the children can be instructed to attempt the two activities on different occasions.

- The children may be allowed more than one evening to complete a homework activity.

- Many of the activities use contexts related to those in the Textbook and Workbook of Heinemann Mathematics 6. The children can be encouraged to explain these contexts to their parents.

- Ideally, the children's homework should be discussed and corrected in school as soon as possible after it has been attempted. Time may be saved by dealing with this in a group situation, correcting and discussing answers to discover who has been experiencing difficulties. An example which has proved difficult for a number of children can be used to revise and reinforce the mathematics underlying it.

- The *Extra* activities are additional work, not necessarily linked to current work in school. They are intended as 'something different' which will be appropriate for children who enjoy such challenges.

## Guidance for Parents

- As the title Home Link-up implies, it is important to explain to parents the purpose of the material and how they can help with their children's mathematics at home.

- *A page of Guidance for Parents is provided on page iv of these notes.* It can be copied and sent to parents when their children start to use Home Link-up. Teachers may also wish to talk to parents about the material when they meet them in school.

- Parents should certainly be encouraged to talk to their children about the homework they are doing. They should be clear that they are not expected to 'teach' and should not exert undue pressure on a child who is experiencing difficulty with a homework task; rather they should be encouraged to make a brief note on the child's homework book.

## Record Sheet

- *A Home Link-up Record Sheet is provided on page v of these notes.* It can be photocopied and attached to the child's homework book.

- Children should indicate on the sheet when a particular activity has been completed.

# Guidance for Parents

Dear Parent,

**Heinemann Mathematics: Home Link-up**

As we believe that regular homework is a valuable part of your child's education we have recently adopted Home Link-up to provide extra practice in mathematics. We expect that it will also give you an insight into the work your child does in school.

Each Home Link-up activity should take your child about 15 to 25 minutes to complete. Most activities will be done in the homework book, though a few are provided as fill-in sheets. The heading for each activity describes its mathematical content, for example,

## Percentages: of a quantity

A few activities will require a calculator.

Home Link-up should help foster a positive attitude to mathematics. Working on their own, children can tackle the activities at their own pace, and develop good study habits.

You can help by talking to your child about the work, praising them and offering help where appropriate. Finally, if your child has problems with the work, don't worry! Just reassure them, and make a brief note in the homework book.

Thank you for your support and co-operation.

# Home Link-up Record Sheet

## Name: _____

## Number

Place value, addition and subtraction: 1  2  3  4  5

Rounding and estimation: 6  7  Calculator  8

Multiplication: 9  10  11  12

Division: 13  14  15  16  17  18  19

Fractions: 20  21  22

Decimals: 23  24  25  26  27

28  29  30  31

Percentages: 32  33

Pattern: 34  35

Multiplication by a 2-digit number: 36  37

Division by a 2-digit number: 38  39

## Measure

Length: 40  41

Weight: 42

Area: 43

Volume: 44

Time: 45  46  47  48  49  50

## Shape

Co-ordinates: 51

2D shape: 52  53  54

Angles: 55

## Handling data

Handling data: 56  57  58  59

Probability: 60

**Heinemann Mathematics 6**

**1** Add or subtract **mentally**.
  **(a)** 72 – 8    **(b)** 56 + 7    **(c)** 143 + 9    **(d)** 220 – 4    **(e)** 305 – 8

Sean found these numbers of frogs near the beach.

42 tree frogs      34 grass frogs      15 grass frogs      55 tree frogs
(spotted)          (spotted)           (green)             (green)

**2** Find **mentally** the total number of
  **(a)** spotted frogs  **(b)** green frogs    **(c)** grass frogs      **(d)** tree frogs.

**3** **(a)** 68 – 33    **(b)** 47 – 25    **(c)** 79 – 32    **(d)** 85 – 65    **(e)** 36 – 23
  **(f)** 35 + 40    **(g)** 49 + 20    **(h)** 64 – 30    **(i)** 72 – 20    **(j)** 94 – 30

**4** Find the missing number.    39 + 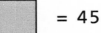 = 45

---

**1** Add **mentally**.
  **(a)** 53 + 28    **(b)** 46 + 44    **(c)** 29 + 29    **(d)** 18 + 47    **(e)** 29 + 16
  **(f)** 37 + 46    **(g)** 17 + 79    **(h)** 26 + 43    **(i)** 49 + 35    **(j)** 68 + 18

**2** The boys did sit-ups on the beach.
  How many did they do altogether?

Roy        Sean

36 sit-ups

28 sit-ups

**3** Subtract **mentally**.
  **(a)** 32 – 18    **(b)** 67 – 48    **(c)** 94 – 37    **(d)** 51 – 26    **(e)** 63 – 19
  **(f)** 70 – 28    **(g)** 55 – 35    **(h)** 83 – 36    **(i)** 43 – 25    **(j)** 91 – 24

**4** The girls did handstands. How many more
  **(a)** did Dorothy do than Elaine?
  **(b)** should each girl do so that
    each does 80 handstands?

Elaine            Dorothy
27 handstands      44 handstands

**1** **(a)** Write Simon's number in figures.

_____

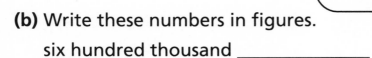

Twenty-six thousand,
six hundred and
fifty-two.

**(b)** Write these numbers in figures.

six hundred thousand _____

three hundred and forty thousand, seven hundred _____

**(c)** Write 206 500 in words. _____

_____

**2** Increase 625 187 by

three thousand        thirty thousand        three hundred thousand

_____        _____        _____

---

**1** Find the first number greater than 106 637 where

**(a)** its tens and units digits are the same _____

**(b)** its thousands and units digits are the same. _____

**2** **(a)** Write Roy's number in figures.

_____

One million, two
hundred and
thirty thousand.

**(b)** Write these numbers in figures.

four million, four hundred thousand, four hundred _____

seven million, seven hundred thousand and seventy _____

**(c)** Write 2 000 002 in words. _____

**3** What is the value of the underlined digit?

1 6<u>3</u>5 479 _____        <u>1</u> 635 479 _____

These are the numbers of fish around the island.

|        |            | Bay  | Cavern |
|--------|------------|------|--------|
| **(a)**| gold fish  | 3247 | 8920   |
| **(b)**| white fish | 8622 | 3491   |
| **(c)**| black fish | 6357 | 3663   |

**1**  Find the total of each type of fish.

**2**  How many more  **(a)** gold fish are in the Cavern than in the Bay?
                       **(b)** white fish are in the Bay than in the Cavern?

**3**  **(a)**   6199      **(b)**   5068      **(c)**   8000      **(d)**   3899
             + 3892              – 2874              – 4601              + 9101

**4**  Find the number of crabs in the
       **(a)** Bay:      6159 + 398 + 6
       **(b)** Cavern:  37 + 5207 + 999

---

**1**  Round **to the nearest ten:**
       **(a)** 157      **(b)** 214      **(c)** 386      **(d)** 93      **(e)** 485
       **(f)** 78       **(g)** 541      **(h)** 909      **(i)** 496     **(j)** 202

Along the beach, there are
178 striped crabs and
54 spotted crabs.

> 178 is **about** 180.
> 54 is **about** 50.
> 180 – 50 = 130,
> so there are **about** 130
> more striped crabs than
> spotted crabs.

**2**  Estimate.
       **(a)** 163 – 47      **(b)** 246 – 29      **(c)** 377 – 32
       **(d)** 128 + 43      **(e)** 71 + 109      **(f)** 254 + 26
       **(g)** 189 – 61      **(h)** 251 – 48      **(i)** 167 + 33

**1**   Round **to the nearest hundred**:   **(a)** 360   **(b)** 236   **(c)** 145
**(d)** 858   **(e)** 450   **(f)** 948

There are 382 pistols and 131 muskets in the sunken galleon.

382 is **about** 400. 131 is **about** 100.
Altogether there are **about 500** guns.

**2**   Estimate **(a)** 111 + 261   **(b)** 130 + 319   **(c)** 175 + 237
**(d)** 422 + 190   **(e)** 340 + 372   **(f)** 306 + 296

There are 412 swords and 187 daggers in the galleon.

412 is **about** 400. 187 is **about** 200.
There are **about 200** more swords than daggers.

**3**   Estimate
**(a)** 292 – 135   **(b)** 717 – 575   **(c)** 186 – 124
**(d)** 650 – 410   **(e)** 581 – 229   **(f)** 999 – 878

---

**1**   Find the number which can be

**(a)** added to   `46341.`   **(b)** added to   `318253.`

to give   `49341.`   to give   `718253.`

**(c)** subtracted from   `58238.`   **(d)** subtracted from   `752392.`

to give   `38238.`   to give   `712392.`

**2 (a)** Which two of these numbers add to make 1 million?

100 550      397 450      601 550      102 550      398 450

**(b)** Which two of these numbers have the smallest difference?

**1 (a)** Start here.
Calculate 9 x 6.
Look for the answer
54 and colour the
answer box.

| **54** |
|---|
| 3 x 5 |

- Now calculate 3 x 5.
  Look for the answer
  and colour the box.
- Continue until you
  colour

| **8** |
|---|
| 9 x 6 |

| **8** | **36** | **32** | **24** | **50** | **15** |
|---|---|---|---|---|---|
| 9 x 6 | 5 x 7 | 7 x 7 | 3 x 4 | 6 x 5 | 2 x 9 |
| **81** | **9** | **7** | **60** | **64** | **14** |
| 4 x 7 | 5 x 10 | 9 x 1 | 3 x 7 | 3 x 9 | 5 x 9 |
| **21** | **16** | **40** | **20** | **54** | **12** |
| 8 x 6 | 7 x 8 | 6 x 10 | 7 x 2 | 3 x 5 | 2 x 8 |
| **27** | **63** | **45** | **56** | **80** | **18** |
| 10 x 8 | 8 x 8 | 9 x 9 | 8 x 1 | 1 x 7 | 6 x 6 |
| **72** | **28** | **35** | **49** | **30** | **48** |
| 8 x 4 | 6 x 4 | 9 x 8 | 4 x 10 | 7 x 9 | 4 x 5 |

**(b)** What do you notice about the pattern of the coloured boxes?

_____

**2** Complete each pattern.

9 x 8 = _____        9 x 1 = _____

8 x 7 = _____        8 x 2 = _____

7 x 6 = _____        7 x 3 = _____

_____ x _____ = _____        _____ x _____ = _____

_____ x _____ = _____        _____ x _____ = _____

**3** Multiply to find the missing numbers.

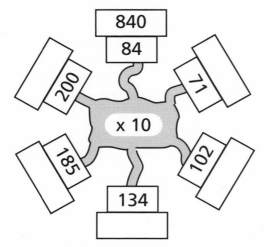

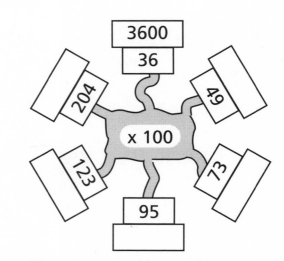

1   Superhero and Mog take food and water
    to the emergency area.
    They give each person
    - 4 l of milk
    - 7 kg of vita-bics
    - 6 kg of dried soup
    - 5 kg of rice
    - 9 l of water.
    How much of each item did Superhero and Mog give?

| milk | vita-bics | dried soup | rice | water |
|------|-----------|------------|------|-------|

2   (a)   3215      (b)   743      (c)   3605      (d)   2089      (e)   863
          x 2             x 8            x 3             x 7            x 9
    _____        _____       _____        _____       _____

    _____        _____       _____        _____       _____

---

Mog buys emergency equipment with the money she has raised.

| water purifier | large tent | generator | mobile surgery |
|----------------|------------|-----------|----------------|
| £1614 | £2030 | £1402 | £2613 |

1   How much does it cost to buy
    (a) 4 water purifiers              (b) 8 tents
    (c) 9 generators                  (d) 5 mobile surgeries?

2   How much does it cost Mog to buy 4125
    packs of sterilising tablets at £8 per pack?

3   Find the cost of
    (a) 1264 boxes of knives at £9
    (b) 2138 boxes of forks at £7
    (c) 3275 boxes of spoons at £5.

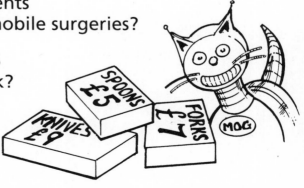

**1** Mog buys these numbers of lucky dip gifts.
 **(a) 1065**          **(b) 3169**          **(c) 2573**          **(d) 2186**

  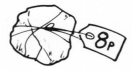 

Find the amount, in **pounds and pence**, spent on each type of gift.

**2** Mog hires fancy dress outfits for the children invited to the party.
 Find how much she pays to hire these costumes.
 **(a)** 20 robots at £3·65
 **(b)** 35 lions at £5·07
 **(c)** 23 Klingons at £4·30
 **(d)** 42 Peter Pans at £6·55

**3**  There are five of the fancy dress outfits in the box, two of one kind and three of another.

Which costumes are in the box?

Problem solving

 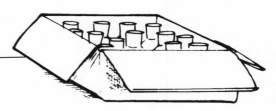

**1** Mog is sorting items at Medic-Aid.
 How many sets are there and how many items are left over?
 **(a)** 13 eyepatches in sets of 2          **(b)** 29 tubes in sets of 3
 **(c)** 25 bottles in sets of 4          **(d)** 34 bandages in sets of 5

**2** **(a)** $26 \div 3$   **(b)** $19 \div 2$   **(c)** $31 \div 4$   **(d)** $18 \div 5$
 **(e)** $4\overline{)22}$   **(f)** $3\overline{)19}$   **(g)** $\frac{1}{2}$ of 16   **(h)** $\frac{1}{5}$ of 40

**3** Which of these numbers are factors of 15?
 (15)  (2)  (5)  (7)  (3)  (4)  (1)  (10)

**4** List all the factors of   **(a)** 14   **(b)** 20

Superhero is packing items for Medic-Aid.

**1**  Share equally. How many are in each
box and how many are left over?
   **(a)** 729 bottles in 2 boxes
   **(b)** 491 tubes in 5 boxes

**2**  **(a)** $652 \div 3$    **(b)** $\frac{1}{4}$ of 356    **(c)** $5 \overline{)817}$

**3**  How many strips are there and how many pills left over?

   **(a)**  2819 in strips of 4

   **(b)** 3203 in strips of 3

**4**  Which of these numbers have
3 **and** 5 as factors?

| 2055 | 5870 | 3270 |

---

Superhero packs jewels into bags.

**1**  How many bags are needed and
how many jewels are left over?
   **(a)** 51 rubies, in bags of 6
   **(b)** 65 opals, in bags of 7

**2**  **(a)** $43 \div 8$    **(b)** $31 \div 7$    **(c)** $50 \div 9$    **(d)** $37 \div 6$
   **(e)** $9 \overline{)67}$    **(f)** $7 \overline{)60}$    **(g)** $\frac{1}{6}$ of 54    **(h)** $\frac{1}{8}$ of 48

**3**  Which of these numbers have
   **(a)** 7 as a factor
   **(b)** 8 as a factor?

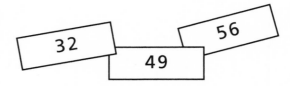

   32    56    49

**4**  Use a rule for dividing by 10 to find
   **(a)** $3827 \div 10$    **(b)** $5600 \div 10$    **(c)** $708 \div 10$    **(d)** $\frac{1}{10}$ of 4060

Superhero returns stolen jewels to the jeweller. He makes rings with them.

**Dazzler**
6 rubies

**Sparkler**
7 diamonds

**Starlight**
8 sapphires

**1**  How many Dazzlers can be made with
  **(a)** 260 rubies       **(b)** 1161 rubies       **(c)** 4235 rubies?

**2**  How many Sparklers can be made with
  **(a)** 1277 diamonds    **(b)** 2839 diamonds    **(c)** 4942 diamonds?

**3**  How many Starlights can be made with
  **(a)** 1721 sapphires   **(b)** 3020 sapphires   **(c)** 7511 sapphires?

**4**  **(a)** $3236 \div 9$   **(b)** $\frac{1}{7}$ of 1064   **(c)** $6\overline{)5224}$   **(d)** $\frac{1}{8}$ of 6112

---

Complete Superhero's puzzle grid.

**Clues**

| **down** | **across** |
|---|---|
| **1** $2\overline{)6834}$ | **3** $5\overline{)1440}$ |
| **2** $6183 \div 9$ | **4** $9096 \div 8$ |
| **3** $\frac{1}{4}$ of 9476 | **5** $\frac{1}{3}$ of 8712 |

1   Use the code to find
Mog's favourite food.
Each letter is the **tens**
digit of each answer.

| | code | |
|---|---|---|
| F = 1 | C = 2 | T = 3 |
| G = 4 | H = 5 | I = 6 |
| S = 7 | P = 8 | A = 9 |

| $6768 \div 6$ | $9485 \div 5$ | $6108 \div 3$ | |
|---|---|---|---|

| $7336 \div 8$ | $7922 \div 2$ | $8253 \div 7$ | $5412 \div 4$ |
|---|---|---|---|

2   Check **by multiplying** to find which of these divisions are wrong.
    **(a)** $4218 \div 3 = 1376$    **(b)** $5382 \div 6 = 897$    **(c)** $9504 \div 9 = 1045$

3
    My number divided by 7 gives 816.
    What is my number?

---

Superhero and Mog look at the
snaps they took at the beach.

**1**   Each boat carried 13 people.
How many boats did we
need for 273 people?

**2**   How many stacks of 9
did I make from 394
deckchairs?

**3**   I gave away 3000
boomerangs. How many
boxes of 34 did I have to buy?

**4**   The train could carry 93
people. How many trips were
needed for 1628 people?

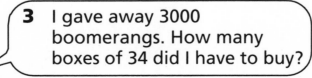

**1** Write equal fractions for each pair of designs.

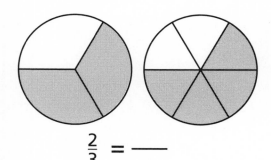
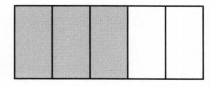
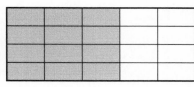

$$\frac{2}{3} = \underline{\quad}$$

$$\underline{\quad} = \underline{\quad}$$

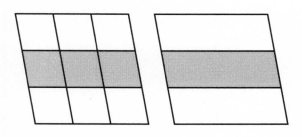
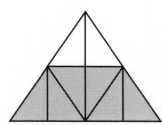

$$\underline{\quad} = \underline{\quad}$$

$$\underline{\quad} = \underline{\quad}$$

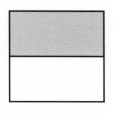

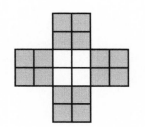

$$\underline{\quad} = \underline{\quad}$$

$$\underline{\quad} = \underline{\quad}$$

**2** Complete.    $\frac{1}{2} = \frac{\phantom{0}}{6}$        $\frac{4}{5} = \frac{\phantom{0}}{10}$        $\frac{2}{3} = \frac{\phantom{0}}{12}$

**3** Complete.    $\frac{6}{9} = \frac{\phantom{0}}{3}$        $\frac{15}{20} = \frac{\phantom{0}}{4}$        $\frac{30}{100} = \frac{\phantom{0}}{10}$

**4** Change    **(a)** $\frac{3}{5}$ to twentieths    **(b)** $\frac{9}{12}$ to quarters    **(c)** $\frac{1}{2}$ to hundredths

_____        _____        _____

**5** Simplify.    $\frac{6}{8} =$        $\frac{4}{10} =$        $\frac{80}{100} =$

4 of the 10 shields have circle designs.

$$\frac{4}{10} = \frac{2}{5}$$

$\frac{2}{5}$ of the shields have circles.

**1** What fraction of the shields have
(a) crosses   (b) stripes?

**2** On another wall, there are 20 flags.
2 are red, 3 are yellow, 5 are blue and 10 are green.
What fraction of the flags are
(a) red   (b) yellow   (c) blue   (d) green?

**3** There are 100 horses in the castle stables.
10 are black, 20 are grey and the rest are chestnut.
What fraction of the horses are
(a) black   (b) grey   (c) chestnut?

80 weapons are stored in the castle armoury.
$\frac{1}{8}$ are longbows.   $\frac{1}{8}$ of 80 = **10**
**10 of the weapons** are longbows.

**1** Find:   (a) $\frac{1}{2}$ of 16   (b) $\frac{1}{4}$ of 36   (c) $\frac{1}{10}$ of 70   (d) $\frac{1}{3}$ of 30
(e) $\frac{1}{7}$ of 42   (f) $\frac{1}{9}$ of 54   (g) $\frac{1}{5}$ of 45   (h) $\frac{1}{8}$ of 64

**2** There are 140 trees growing in Castle Wood.
$\frac{1}{2}$ of them are oak, $\frac{1}{4}$ are elm, $\frac{1}{5}$ are beech and $\frac{1}{10}$ are ash.
How many of the trees are (a) oak (b) elm (c) beech (d) ash?

**3** Find:   (a) $\frac{1}{2}$ of 486   (b) $\frac{1}{2}$ of 472   (c) $\frac{1}{3}$ of 177   (d) $\frac{1}{4}$ of 232
(e) $\frac{1}{8}$ of 376   (f) $\frac{1}{10}$ of 250   (g) $\frac{1}{7}$ of 301   (h) $\frac{1}{9}$ of 459

**1** Colour to match.

( 43 tenths )  ( 5·1 )  ( 9 tenths )  ( 12·6 )  ( 3·0 )  ( 5 units and 1 tenth )

( 30 tenths )  ( 4 units and 3 tenths )  ( 0·9 )  ( three units and no tenths )

( twelve and six tenths )  ( 4·3 )  ( 51 tenths )  ( no units and nine tenths )

**2** Write in decimal form.

**(a)** two units and five tenths _____

**(b)** eleven and three tenths _____

**(c)** forty and one tenth _____

**(d)** twenty-six and nine tenths _____

**3** Arrange in order, starting with the smallest.

14·5    15·4    13·4    14·3    15·0 _____

*Extra*

**You need matches or straws.**

**1** Move 2 matches to make 5 identical squares. Draw the squares.

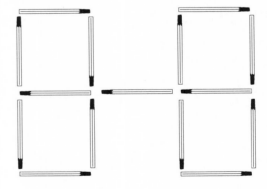

**2** Take away 3 matches to leave 3 triangles.

Sketch the triangles.

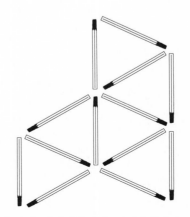

Stan delivers seafood to Bridge Hotel.

**1** Find the total weight of
 **(a)** squid and mussels
 **(b)** lobsters and crabs
 **(c)** all four boxes.

**2** **(a)**    5·8     **(b)**    4·2     **(c)**    16·5     **(d)** 20·2 − 14·3     **(e)** 30·0 − 19·6
        − 2·3           − 0·6            − 8·8

**3** **(a)** 9·6 + 1·7          **(b)** 15·6 + 37·4          **(c)** 12·4 + 7·5 + 28

**4** Stan delivers 25 kg of prawns to Bridge Hotel.
 17·3 kg are used. How many kilograms are left?

**5** Find the difference between 50 kg and 19·1 kg.

---

**1** Multiply to find the total weight.
 **(a)**                    **(b)**                    **(c)**

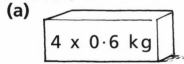
4 x 0·6 kg

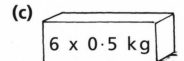
8 x 0·9 kg

6 x 0·5 kg

**2** **(a)** 9 x 3·4     **(b)** 5 x 6·5     **(c)** 2·8 x 7

**3** Check these examples mentally. Correct the answers which are wrong.
 **(a)** 3·7 x 10 = 370     **(b)** 138 ÷ 10 = 1·38     **(c)** 11·8 x 10 = 118
 **(d)** 95 ÷ 10 = 950      **(e)** 2·0 x 10 = 0·2       **(f)** 124 ÷ 10 = 12·4

**4** The fish are shared equally among the boxes.
 Find the weight of fish in each box.
 **(a)** 55·2 kg among 8 boxes
 **(b)** 99·4 kg among 7 boxes
 **(c)** 65·2 kg among 4 boxes
 **(d)** 94·5 kg among 9 boxes
 **(e)** 71·5 kg among 5 boxes

This sign has 100 squares.
The fraction of the sign lit is

57 hundredths or $\frac{57}{100}$ or 0·57

**1** Write each of these fractions in two other ways:

(a) 42 hundredths _____ _____     (b) $\frac{34}{100}$ _____ _____

(c) 30 hundredths _____ _____     (d) 0·47 _____ _____

(e) 7 hundredths _____ _____      (f) 0·09 _____ _____

**2** Write these decimals in order, starting with the smallest.
0·32, 0·02, 0·23, 0·30, 0·22, 0·33

_____

**3** (a) Colour to
show 1·28

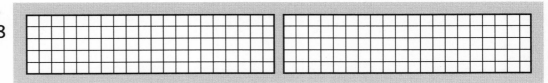

(b) Colour to
show 2·72

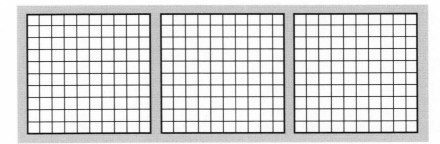

**4** Write in decimal form:

(a) 5 units and 11 hundredths _____     (b) 3 units and 62 hundredths _____

(c) 4 units and 70 hundredths _____     (d) 5 units and 4 hundredths _____

**5** Use the digits  ⬚1⬚  ⬚4⬚  ⬚9⬚  and a decimal point each time.

Write as many different decimals as you can between 2 and 20.

_____

_____

**1** Write each of these in decimal form.
   **(a)** 3 tenths and 8 hundredths     **(b)** 6 tenths and 9 hundredths
   **(c)** 7 tenths and 5 hundredths     **(d)** 0 tenths and 3 hundredths

**2** Write each of these as tenths and hundredths.
   **(a)** 0·35     **(b)** 0·56     **(c)** 0·27     **(d)** 0·40     **(e)** 0·01

**3**   | 0·17 = 1 tenth and 7 hundredths = 0·1 + 0·07 |

   Write these in the same way.
   **(a)** 0·42     **(b)** 0·21     **(c)** 0·96

**4** Write the value of each circled digit.
   **(a)** 31·2⑤     **(b)** 4⑤·37     **(c)** ⑤7·03     **(d)** 27·⑤1

**5** Which of these numbers are **between** 3·4 and 4·3?
   0·43     3·43     34·3     4·03     3·34     4·34

---

**1** **(a)**   0·52        **(b)**   0·06        **(c)**   2·69
          +0·26              +0·96              +1·43
       ‾‾‾‾‾‾              ‾‾‾‾‾‾              ‾‾‾‾‾‾

   **(d)** 4·53 + 3·87     **(e)** 23·8 + 1·46     **(f)** 36·77 + 21·46

**2** What is the price of
   each cake with cream?

*Ferry Cakes*

carrot £1·18     lemon £1·20
chocolate £1·24     apple £1·05

cream 38p     coffee £1·15

**3** What is the total cost of each order?

**(a)**
| *Ferry Cakes* |
| carrot cake |
| apple cake |
| coffee |

**(b)**
| *Ferry Cakes* |
| chocolate cake |
| cream |
| coffee |

**1** **(a)** $\begin{array}{r} 8\cdot35 \\ -\ 3\cdot18 \\ \hline \end{array}$    **(b)** $\begin{array}{r} 21\cdot04 \\ -\ 10\cdot68 \\ \hline \end{array}$    **(c)** $\begin{array}{r} 19\cdot23 \\ -\ 9\cdot47 \\ \hline \end{array}$    **(d)** $\begin{array}{r} 42\cdot5 \\ -\ 12\cdot63 \\ \hline \end{array}$

**(e)** 20·34 − 14·69    **(f)** 32·6 − 13·64    **(g)** 41 − 10·67

**2** **(a)** Mr Thomson's car is 3·15 metres long. How much shorter is this than 3·55 metres?

**(b)** What is Mr Thomson's change from £20 after paying for the ferry?

**3** **(a)** Mrs Stuart's van is 4·82 metres long. How much longer is this than 3·55 metres?

**(b)** What is Mrs Stuart's change from £50?

*Special weekend offer*

**Alltmouth Ferry**
Charge for any vehicle and driver.
• vehicles shorter than 3·55m £13·75
• vehicles longer than 3·55m £15·50

---

**1** A boat is 5·65 metres long. The trailer is 0·5 metres longer. How long is the trailer?

**2** Jeff's car is 4·89 metres long and his trailer is 7·15 metres long.

**(a)** What is the total length of the car and trailer?

**(b)** Bill's car and trailer have a total length of 13·14 metres. Is this longer or shorter than Jeff's and by how much?

**3** **(a)** 7 x 3·6    **(b)** 4·8 x 6    **(c)** 60·3 ÷ 9    **(d)** 47·2 ÷ 8

**4** On Wednesday Jill and Jake caught salmon with these weights:

4·4 kg        4·5 kg        5·2 kg        3·5 kg

**(a)** Find the difference in weight between the heaviest and the lightest salmon.

**(b)** What is the total weight of salmon?

**(c)** What is the average weight of a salmon?

The height of the cliff at the lighthouse was
measured at different points.

|                   | at A  | at B  | at C  | at D  | at E  |
|-------------------|-------|-------|-------|-------|-------|
| **height in metres** | 18·53 | 16·07 | 19·24 | 17·39 | 15·62 |

**1** **(a)** Which point on the cliff is ● highest ● lowest?

**(b)** What is the difference in height between these points?

**(c)** What is the average height of the five points **to the nearest metre?**

**2** There are 109 steps from the beach to the lighthouse.
Each step is 0·17 metres in height.
At which point, A, B, C, D or E, do you think the
steps reach the top of the cliff? Explain.

**3** **(a)** Enter a 3-digit starting number with 2 decimal places.
Then → multiply by 30 → add 18·36 → divide by 6
→ multiply by 2 → subtract 6·12

**(b)** Do all this again for different starting numbers.
What do you notice about the start and finish numbers each time?

Problem
solving

## Extra

● Cut out the six triangles.
● Fit them together to make a hexagon.
The pair of numbers at
each join must add to 10.

Stick the hexagon in your homework book.

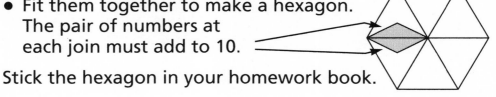

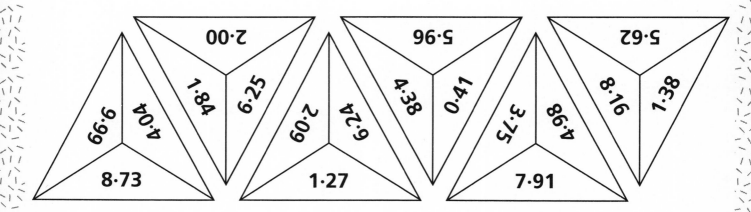

Each floor design has 100 tiles.

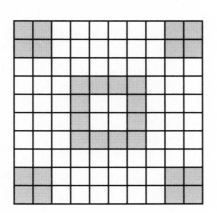
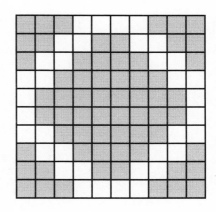

**1**  Complete.

shaded → $\frac{28}{100}$ or _____%        shaded → _____ or _____%

not shaded → _____ or _____%        not shaded → _____ or _____%

**2  (a)** Complete:  5% = $\frac{\phantom{00}}{100}$     20% = $\frac{\phantom{00}}{100}$     30% = $\frac{\phantom{00}}{100}$     40% = $\frac{\phantom{00}}{100}$

**(b)** Colour:
5% red, 20% blue, 30% green and 40% yellow

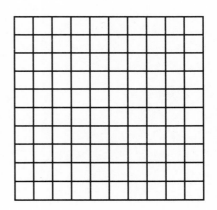

**(c)** What percentage
is not coloured? _____

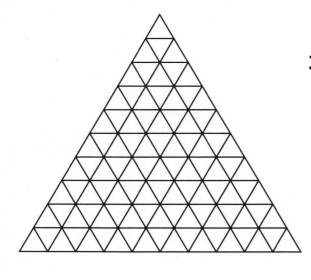

**3  (a)** Use red, blue and green to
colour your own design.

**(b)** Complete.

_____ % is coloured red

_____ % is coloured blue

_____ % is coloured green

**1** Copy and complete.   $10\% = \frac{1}{10}$   $50\% = $ —   $25\% = $ —

**2** Find **(a)** 25% of 12   **(b)** 10% of 30   **(c)** 50% of 4
   **(d)** 10% of 90   **(e)** 50% of 100   **(f)** 25% of 20

**3** Which is more? **(a)** 25% of 28 **or** 10% of 80
   **(b)** 50% of 18 **or** 25% of 32

**4** At the castle banquet there are 240 guests.
   25% choose pheasant,
   50% choose venison,
   10% choose trout.
   **(a)** How many guests choose
   • pheasant • venison • trout?
   **(b)** The rest of the guests choose salad.
   What **percentage** choose salad?

Complete each function machine.

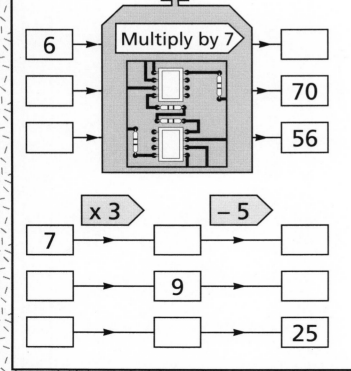

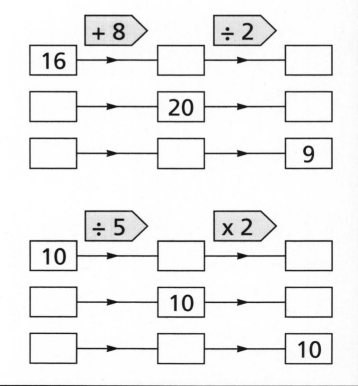

**1  (a)** Draw the next two matchstick flag patterns.

1

2

3

4

5

**(b)** Complete.

| Number of flags | Number of matches |
|:---:|:---:|
| 1 | → 5 |
| 2 | → |
| 3 | |
| 4 | |
| 5 | |

**(c)** How many matches are needed for

- 8 flags _____
- 10 flags _____
- 20 flags? _____

**(d)** Complete.
The number of matches is _____ times the number of flags.

**2  (a)** Complete.

| Number of shields | Number of swords |
|:---:|:---:|
| 1 | → 2 |
| 2 | |
| 3 | |
| 4 | |
| 5 | |

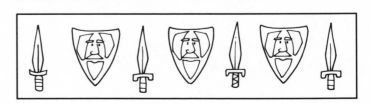

**(b)** How many swords are needed for  • 7 shields _____  • 10 shields _____?

The number of swords is _____

**1** Find the number of passengers
the Deltawing can carry on
(a) 15 flights
(b) 18 flights.

**Deltawing 37 passengers**

**2** Find the number of passengers
the Airtaxi can carry on
(a) 14 flights
(b) 17 flights.

**Airtaxi 56 passengers**

**3** Which is cheaper and by how much?
(a) 19 children flying to Endley
**or**
(b) 13 children flying to Carra.

**FLY AEROBLOT**
*CHEAP RATES FOR CHILDREN*
ENDLEY - £42   CARRA - £61

**1** (a) Find the total value
of a box of watches.
(b) How many watches
are in 25 boxes?

24 WATCHES

£47 EACH

**2** (a) Find the total value
of a box of necklaces.
(b) How many necklaces
are in 59 boxes?

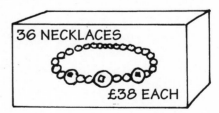

36 NECKLACES

£38 EACH

**3** (a) Selma is paid £76 per day.
How much is she paid for 45 days?
(b) Tracy is paid £95 per day.
How much is she paid for 33 days?

**1**  Copy and complete these divisions.

**(a)**                    **(b)**                    **(c)**

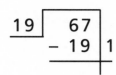

$$19 \overline{)\ 67}$$
$$-\ 19\ \ |\ 1$$

$$57 \overline{)171}$$

$$85 \overline{)173}$$

**2**  Share equally. How many does each
    passenger receive?
    How many are
    left over?

AEROBLOT
AIRLINES

**(a)** 140 sandwiches
    among 46
    passengers

**(b)** 135 drinks
    among 58
    passengers

---

**1**  Divide.  **(a)** $26 \overline{)317}$    **(b)** $15 \overline{)195}$    **(c)** $850 \div 28$

**2**  There are 565 passengers to go through Customs
    in groups of 25.

**(a)** How many groups of 25 are there?

**(b)** How many passengers are left to go
    through in a smaller group?

**3**  There are 47 passport officers on
    duty to stamp 565 passports.

**(a)** How many passports should
    each officer stamp if they
    share the work equally?

**(b)** The Chief Officer stamps
    the remainder.
    How many does he stamp?

# Extra

**Use a calculator.**

**1** Complete.   **(a)** 21 x 24 = _____   **(b)** 13 x 62 = _____

   12 x 42 = _____   31 x 26 = _____

**2** There are other sets of numbers like this.
Find the missing digit and the product for each of these.

**(a)** 12 x 6☐ = _____   **(b)** 23 x 9☐ = _____

   21 x ☐6 = _____   32 x ☐9 = _____

---

| Heinemann Mathematics 6    Home Link-up<br>Textbook pages 69 and 70 | Length: addition, subtraction, perimeter | **40** |
| --- | --- | --- |

**1** Find the total length
of wood needed to
make this perch.

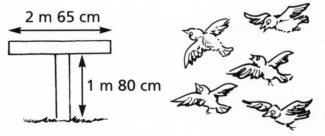

**2** Find the difference in the lengths of these perches.

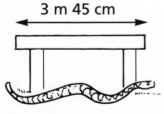
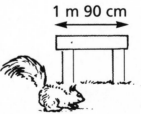

**3** Find the perimeter of each enclosure.

**(a)**

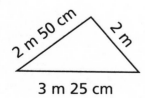

**(b)**

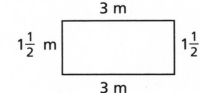

**(c)**

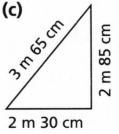

**4** Find the perimeter of a square with a side length of
**(a)** 5 m   **(b)** 75 cm   **(c)** 2 m 40 cm   **(d)** 2 m 4 cm

**2** Each animal has been drawn to a different scale.
Measure each animal, then calculate its true length.

**(a) 1 cm to 8 cm**

**(b) 1 cm to 20 cm**

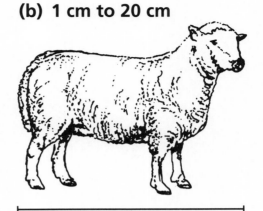

**(c) 1 cm to 40 cm**

**(d) 1 cm to 50 cm**

**2 (a)** Find the true height of the giraffe.

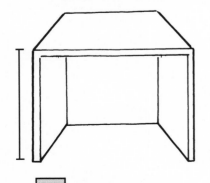

**1 cm to 2 m**

**(b)** In which of these shelters could
the giraffe stand upright? Explain.

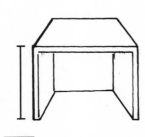

**A** **1 cm to 3 m**        **B** **1 cm to 4 m**        **C** **1 cm to 80 cm**

**1** Debbie is weighing food for the animals.
What weight is shown on each scale?

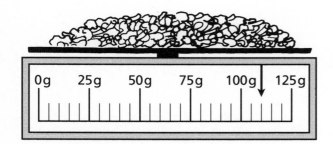

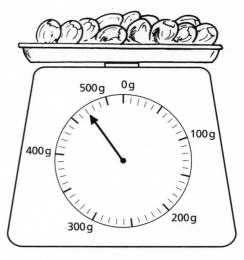

The grapes weigh _____.

The nuts weigh _____.

**2** Read the scales to the nearest mark to find the weights of these foods.

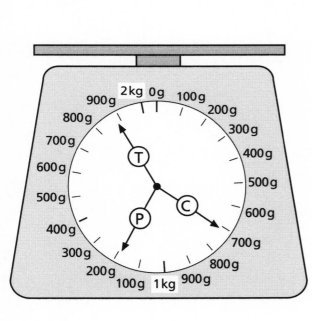

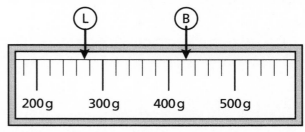

ⓒ cabbage _____

Ⓟ parsnip _____

Ⓣ turnip _____

Ⓛ lettuce _____

Ⓑ bamboo shoots _____

**3** On the scales, draw pointers to show the weight of each food.

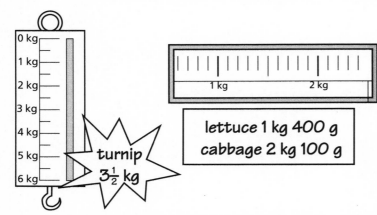

turnip
$3\frac{1}{2}$ kg

lettuce 1 kg 400 g
cabbage 2 kg 100 g

nuts 250 g
dates 375 g

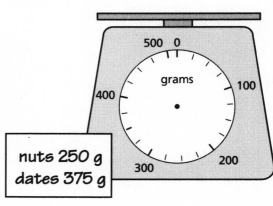

**1**  Find the area, in squares, of each rectangle.

**(a)**

Area = _____ squares

**(b)**

Area = _____

**2**  Find each area, in squares.

**(a)**

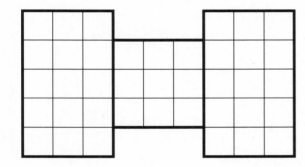

Area = _____

**(b)**

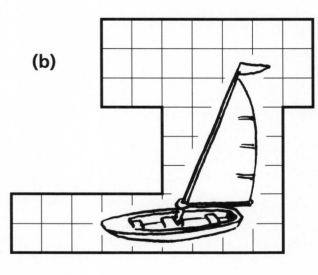

Area = _____

**(c)**

Area = _____

**(d)**

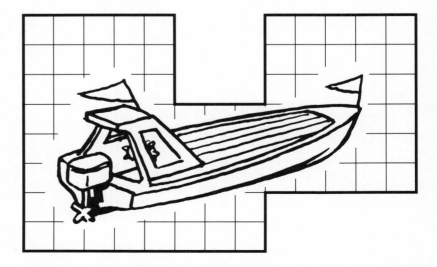

Area = _____

**1**   What is the volume, in millilitres, of medicine in each bottle?

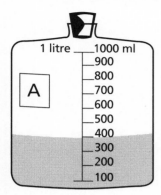
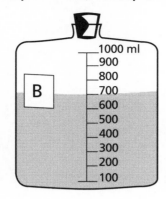
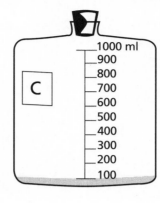

_____          _____          _____

**2**   Which bottle contains   **(a)** more than $\frac{1}{2}$ litre _____

                                        **(b)** between $\frac{1}{4}$ litre and $\frac{1}{2}$ litre? _____

**3**   **(a)** Complete each scale by writing a volume beside each mark.

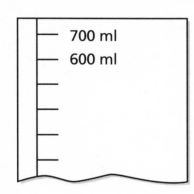
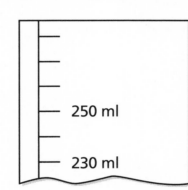
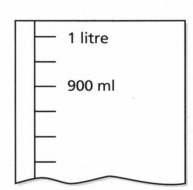

   **(b)** Colour the scales to show each volume.
     • fruit juice 400 ml   • cough mixture 270 ml   • antiseptic 850 ml

**4**   Read each volume **to the nearest mark.**

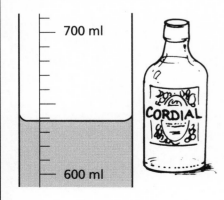
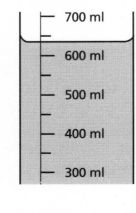

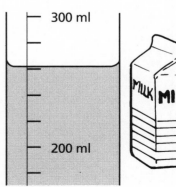

_____          _____          _____

Channel 6TV studio tours
| | |
|---|---|
| A | 9.15 am - 9.50 am |
| B | 10.25 am - 11.30 am |
| C | 2.45 pm - 3.30 pm |
| D | 3.35 pm - 4.55 pm |

**1** How long does each tour last?

**2** Zara arrived at Channel 6 at quarter to twelve.
She took the next available tour and left when it finished.
**(a)** When did it finish?        **(b)** How long was she at Channel 6?

**3** This record sheet shows when two TV stars
arrived at, and left, the 6TV studios.
**(a)** How long did each spend at the studios?
**(b)** For how long were **both** in the building
**at the same time**?

| Freda Star | arr. 9.20 am |
|---|---|
| | dep. 12.10 pm |
| Clint Logan | arr. 11.20 am |
| | dep. 2.25 pm |

---

**1** Reg makes videotape copies of some 6TV programmes.
When does he finish making each copy?

| | Programme | starts copying at | time taken to copy |
|---|---|---|---|
| **(a)** | *Starburst* | 11.30 am | 2 hours |
| **(b)** | *Sport Now* | 2.15 pm | 45 minutes |
| **(c)** | *Timewarp* | 4.40 pm | 40 minutes |

**2** Maxine finds the running times of four films to be shown on 6TV.

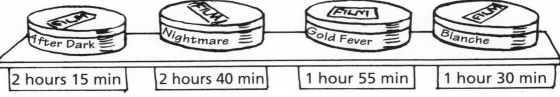

| 2 hours 15 min | 2 hours 40 min | 1 hour 55 min | 1 hour 30 min |

She makes a list of the times when the films will start.
*After Dark* – Monday 6.30 pm        *Nightmare* – Wednesday 3.05 pm
*Gold Fever* – Friday 9.20 am        *Blanche* – Saturday 11.00 pm
When will each film finish?

**1**  Find the starting times for each rehearsal.

|       |               | rehearsal   | finishing time |
|-------|---------------|-------------|----------------|
| **(a)** | *Popscene*      | 2 hours     | 3.45 pm        |
| **(b)** | *Play for Today* | 3 hours     | 2.15 pm        |
| **(c)** | *News*          | 25 minutes  | 4.00 pm        |
| **(d)** | *Quiztime*      | 50 minutes  | 8.55 pm        |

**2**  Doors open 40 minutes before each programme starts

|          | programme starts |
|----------|------------------|
| Studio 1 | 10.50 am         |
| Studio 2 | 11.15 am         |
| Studio 3 | 12.00            |

Find when each studio opens its doors to the public.

**3**  A 6TV crew stopped filming at 3.15 pm after spending 4 hours 20 minutes trying to film a rare animal. When did the crew start filming?

---

**1**  Change each time to a 24-hour time.
**(a)** 6.15 am   **(b)** 6.00 pm   **(c)** 1.05 pm   **(d)** 11.00 pm   **(e)** 5.50 am

**2**  Change each time to a 12-hour time. Use am or pm.
**(a)** 14.00   **(b)** 01.00   **(c)** 17.45   **(d)** 09.10   **(e)** 12.00

| Monday           | 6TV |
|------------------|-----|
| 11.45 *Cartoon Time* |     |
| 12.15 *Travelscene*  |     |
| 1.05 *Lunchdate*     |     |
| 3.10 *Film on 6*     |     |
| 4.50 *News*          |     |
| 5.00 *Weather*       |     |
| 5.03 *Quickquiz*     |     |
| 5.35 *Cooking for Two* |   |

**3**  Write each programme time as a 24-hour time.

**4**  John's video recorder has a 24-hour clock. Which programme is he recording when the video clock shows
**(a)** 12.00   **(b)** 13.30   **(c)** 16.55?

**5**  Which starting time should John set on his video to record
**(a)** *Film on 6*
**(b)** *Cooking for Two*?

**1**   Use the notices. Complete the schedule for Tuesday afternoon.

| Tuesday afternoon programmes 6TV | |
|---|---|
| *Red Dragon* | 11.59 |
| *News* | |
| | 13.25 |
| | |
| *Art Facts* | 14.28 |
| | |
| *Buzzword* | 16.07 |
| *Popview* | |
| | |

**2**   Name the programme which starts at

16.40 _____      15.15 _____

**3**   Which programme is showing at

13.20 _____      14.00? _____

**4**   Which programme starts
just before 2.30 pm                    just after 4.05 pm?

_____              _____

**5**   There was picture interference for
one hour, starting at 13.35.
   **(a)** When did the interference end? _____
   **(b)** Which programmes were affected?

_____

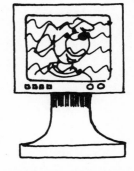

Problem solving

Complete Antonia's schedule for these programmes.

| *Backstreet* | *You Are Not Alone* |
|---|---|
| $1\frac{1}{2}$ hours | 1 hour 40 minutes |

| *Alive and sleeping* | *Doctor Ned* |
|---|---|
| 40 minutes | 30 minutes |

**Problem solving**

**6TV** — **Tuesday**

| Start | Programme | Finish |
|---|---|---|
| 17.45 | | 18.15 |
| 18.15 | *Alive and Sleeping* | |
| | *You Are Not Alone* | |
| | | |

# Extra

Which presenters left the 6TV studios at the same time? Explain.

| **Saturday afternoon** | |
|---|---|
| *Look Sharp* | 12.00 |
| *News* | 13.00 |
| *Waves* | 13.45 |
| *Crossquiz* | 14.05 |
| *Chat Show* | 14.15 |
| *All Right!* | 15.10 |
| *Cartoon Fun* | 15.40 |

**Tracey**

I left 40 minutes after the *Chat Show* finished.

**Bill**

I went home 25 minutes before the start of *Cartoon Fun.*

I presented *Crossquiz.* I left $1\frac{1}{2}$ hours after it was finished.

**Ann**

**Desmond**

I arrived at 2.50 pm to present the next show. I left as soon as it was finished.

I arrived just in time to present *Waves.* I left 2 hours later.

**Shareen**

**1**   Write the co-ordinates of each Star Freighter shown on the computer screen.

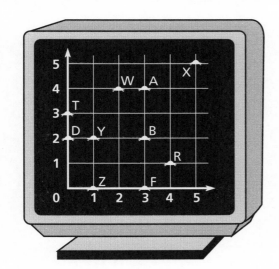

**Star Freighters' Co-ordinates**

A ( ___ , ___ )   B _____

D _____   F _____

R _____   T _____

W _____   X _____

Y _____   Z _____

**2**   Mark these points on the grid below. Join them, **in order,** with straight lines, to make a picture of a Star Freighter.

Star Freighter X:   (5,4)   (7,5)   (9,5)   (9,4)   (13,4)   (18,6)   (17,3)   (18,2)
(15,1)   (10,1)   (5,0)   (5,1)   (0,3)   (3,4) and back to (5,4)

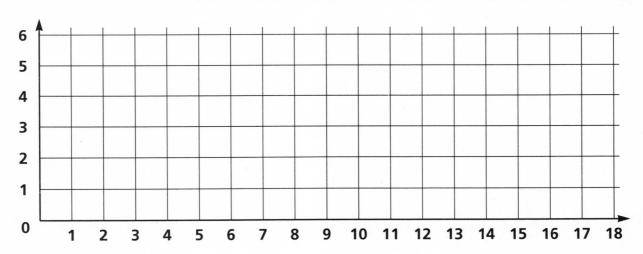

**3   (a)** Mark these points. Join them, in order, to make half of a symmetrical picture.
(1,3)  (1,4)  (2,5)  (4,3)  (5,4)
(6,3)  (8,5)  (9,4)  (9,3)

**(b)** Draw the other half and list the co-ordinates in order.

_____

_____

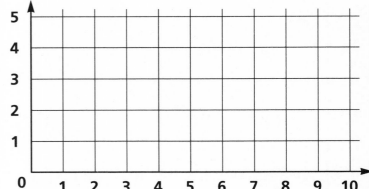

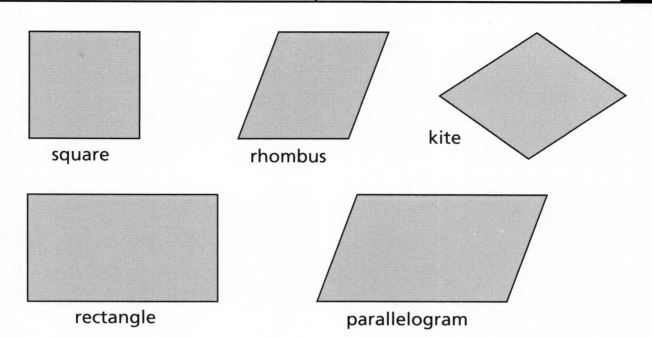

square      rhombus      kite

rectangle      parallelogram

**1** Which shapes have

• no lines of symmetry _____

• only one line of symmetry _____

• only two lines of symmetry _____

• four lines of symmetry? _____

**2** Draw the diagonals on each shape.

**3** Which shapes have a diagonal which is also a line of symmetry?

_____

**4** Cut out this kite. Cut along its longer
diagonal. Use the pieces to make a
shape which has no lines of symmetry.
Stick the shape below.

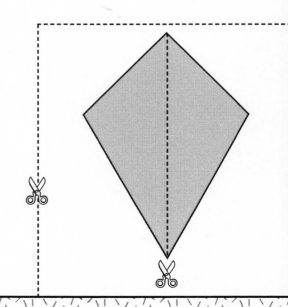

**You need the six-piece tangram.** Make each shape.
Draw round the pieces to show how you did this.

Use 5 pieces.

Use 4 pieces.

Use 4 pieces.

Use all 6 pieces.

Use the
- medium triangle,
- and the two small congruent triangles.

Use the
- rectangle,
- and the two large congruent triangles.

Use
- one large triangle,
- two small congruent triangles,
- the medium triangle
- and the rectangle.

**Six-piece tangrams for activity** 53 .

**1** Trace each shape and mark one corner.
Find how often the shape fits its outline in one full turn.

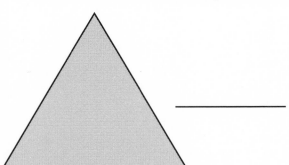

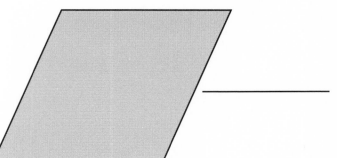

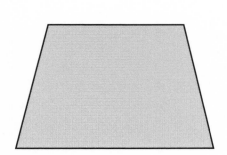

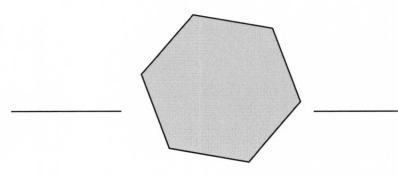

**2** Trace each design and shade it as shown.
Find how often the shaded design fits in one full turn.

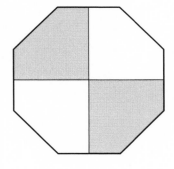

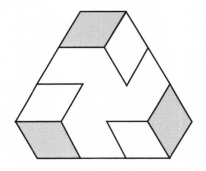

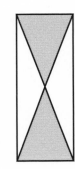

**3** Colour this shape so that the coloured design fits its outline
   ● in two ways      ● in three ways.

Problem solving

**There are two sheets
for this activity.**

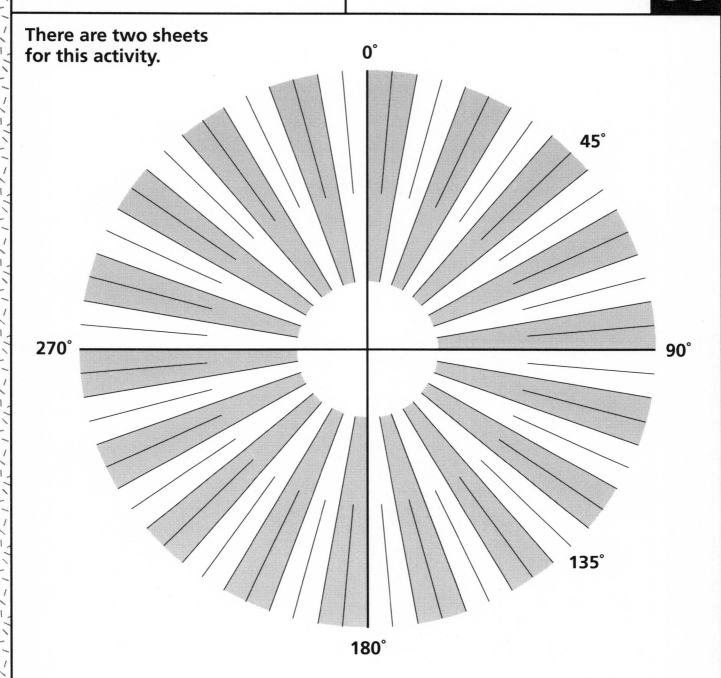

**1**   Look at the angles on the top part of the other sheet.
Label each angle **acute, right** or **obtuse**.

**2**   **(a)** Cut out the shaded pieces from the **bottom** part of the other sheet.
**(b)** Measure each angle using the diagram above.
Record like this:   **Angle W   acute   40˚**

**3**   Write the letters for
**(a) one** pair of angles which make a **right** angle
**(b) two** pairs of angles, where each pair makes a **straight** angle.

**1**

There are two sheets
for this activity.

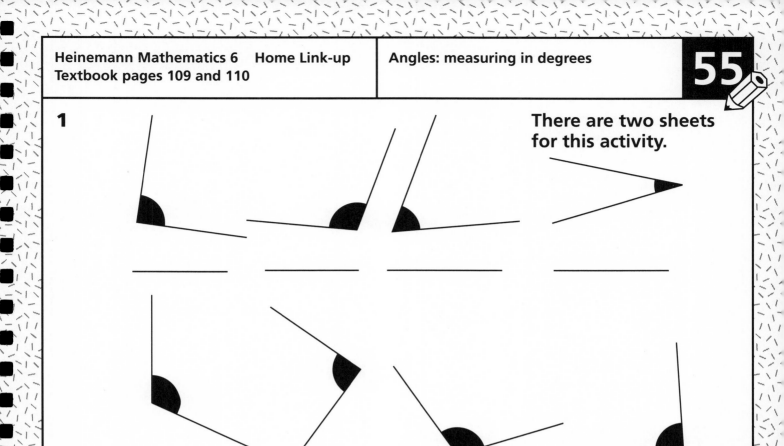

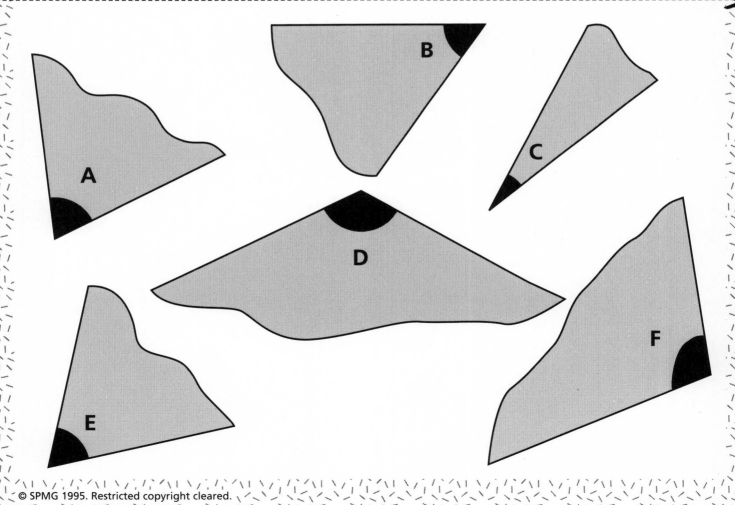

Class 6 buys some of Topperton Garden Centre's heathers.

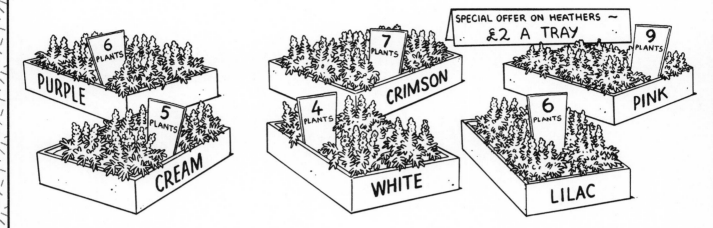

**1** Complete this table to show how many heathers of each colour the children bought.

| Heather colour | white | cream | pink | lilac | purple | crimson |
|---|---|---|---|---|---|---|
| **Number of trays** | 9 | 8 | 8 | 9 | 8 | 10 |
| **Number in 1 tray** | | | | | | |
| **Total number of plants** | | | | | | |

**2** Complete the bar-line graph to show the number of heathers bought by Class 6.

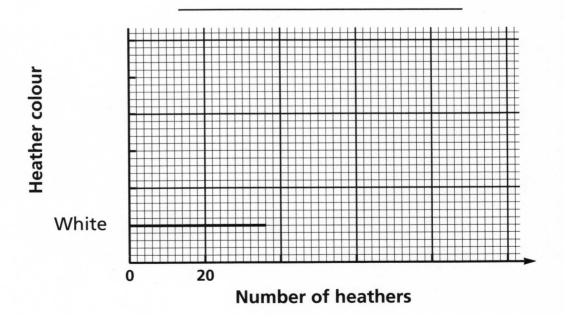

**3** Write a question about your graph for a friend to answer.

_____

_____

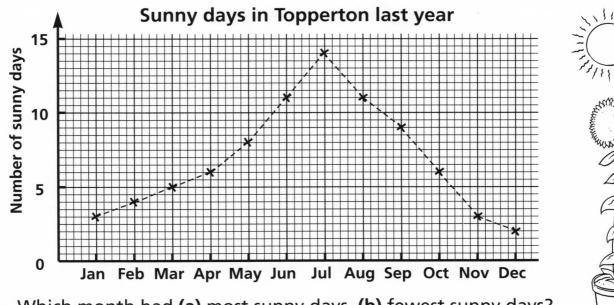

**Sunny days in Topperton last year**

1  Which month had **(a)** most sunny days  **(b)** fewest sunny days?

2  How many sunny days were there in **(a)** February **(b)** November?

3  In which months was the number of sunny days   **(a)** 6   **(b)** more than 8?

4  Write about the trend the graph shows.

These measurements were taken by children in Class 6.

| How far we can jump, in centimetres | | | | |
|---|---|---|---|---|
| Lyn – 142 | Richard – 151 | Sandra – 148 | Aziz – 143 | Sue – 148 |
| Kathryn – 142 | Abdul – 152 | Alan – 153 | Sam – 150 | Patricia – 151 |
| Sarah – 148 | Iona – 153 | John – 156 | | |

1  Complete: The distances jumped range from _____ to _____ .

2  Write the distances jumped, in order, starting with the shortest.

___ , ___ , ___ , ___ , ___ , ___ , ___ , ___ , ___ , ___ , ___ , ___ , ___

3  What distance is  ● the mode _____  ● the median? _____

4  Calculate the mean distance jumped. _____

**1**  Carry out a survey to find which is the most common car colour. Complete this table for the **first 50** cars you see.

| Colour | Tally marks | Total |
|--------|-------------|-------|
| black  |             |       |
| white  |             |       |
| red    |             |       |
| blue   |             |       |
| green  |             |       |
| other  |             |       |
| **Total** |          | 50    |

**2**  Use your data to complete this bar graph.

**Colours of 50 cars**

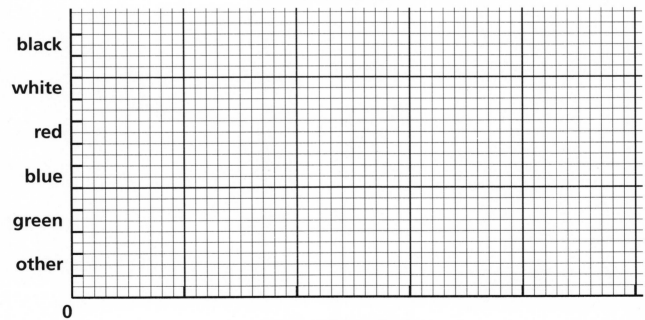

**Number of cars**

**3**  At school, look at the graphs drawn by the others in your group. Write about what you notice.

_____

_____

_____

The table shows the possible ways of choosing **two of the white shapes.**

| cube | 2 | 1 |
|---|---|---|
| sphere | 0 | 1 |

1   Complete the table to show all the possible ways of choosing **two of the grey shapes.**

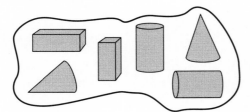

| cuboid | | | | | |
|---|---|---|---|---|---|
| cylinder | | | | | |
| cone | | | | | |

2   Complete this table to show all the possible ways of choosing **one white shape and one grey shape.**

| cube | | | | |
|---|---|---|---|---|
| sphere | | | | |
| cuboid | | | | |
| cylinder | | | | |
| cone | | | | |

# Answers

## 1

**1** (a) 64      (b) 63      (c) 152      (d) 216
    (e) 297

**2** (a) 76 spotted frogs      (b) 70 green frogs
    (c) 49 grass frogs       (d) 97 tree frogs

**3** (a) 35      (b) 22      (c) 47      (d) 20
    (e) 13      (f) 75      (g) 69      (h) 34
    (i) 52      (j) 64

**4** 6

## 2

**1** (a) 81      (b) 90      (c) 58      (d) 65
    (e) 45      (f) 83      (g) 96      (h) 69
    (i) 84      (j) 86

**2** 64 sit-ups

**3** (a) 14      (b) 19      (c) 57      (d) 25
    (e) 44      (f) 42      (g) 20      (h) 47
    (i) 18      (j) 68

**4** (a) 17 more
    (b) Elaine – 53 handstands,
       Dorothy – 36 handstands

---

**1** (a) Write Simon's number in figures.
       *26 652*

> Twenty-six thousand, six hundred and fifty-two.

    (b) Write these numbers in figures.
       six hundred thousand *600 000*
       three hundred and forty thousand, seven hundred *340 700*

    (c) Write 206 500 in words. *two hundred and six thousand, five hundred*

**2** Increase 625 187 by

| three thousand | thirty thousand | three hundred thousand |
|---|---|---|
| *628 187* | *655 187* | *925 187* |

---

**1** Find the first number greater than 106 637 where
    (a) its tens and units digits are the same   *106 644*
    (b) its thousands and units digits are the same.   *106 646*

**2** (a) Write Sean's number in figures.
       *1 230 000*

> One million, two hundred and thirty thousand.

    (b) Write these numbers in figures.
       four million, four hundred thousand, four hundred   *4 400 400*
       seven million, seven hundred thousand and seventy   *7 700 070*
    (c) Write 2 000 002 in words.   *two million and two*

**3** What is the value of the underlined digit?
    1 6<u>3</u>5 479 *thirty thousand*     <u>1</u> 635 479   *one million*

## 5

**1** (a) 12 167 gold fish
    (b) 12 113 white fish
    (c) 10 020 black fish

**2** (a) 5673 more          (b) 5131 more

**3** (a) 10 091   (b) 2194    (c) 3399     (d) 13 000

**4** (a) 6563 crabs         (a) 6243 crabs

## 6

**1** (a) 160       (b) 210          (c) 390
    (d) 90        (e) 480 or 490   (f) 80
    (g) 540      (h) 910         (i) 500
    (j) 200

**2** (a) about 110       (b) about 220
    (c) about 350       (d) about 170
    (e) about 180       (f) about 280
    (g) about 130       (h) about 200
    (i) about 200

## 7

**1** **(a)** 400      **(b)** 200      **(c)** 100
    **(d)** 900      **(e)** 400 or 500      **(f)** 900

**2** **(a)** about 400      **(b)** about 400
    **(c)** about 400      **(d)** about 600
    **(e)** about 700      **(f)** about 600

**3** **(a)** about 200      **(b)** about 100
    **(c)** about 100
    **(d)** about 200 or about 300
    **(e)** about 400      **(f)** about 100

**1** **(a)** 3000      **(b)** 400 000      **(c)** 20 000
    **(d)** 40 000

**2** **(a)** 601 550 and 398 450
    **(b)** 398 450 and 397 450 (difference is 1000)

---

**1 (a)** Start here.
Calculate 9 x 6.
Look for the answer
54 and colour the
answer box.

| 54 |
|----|
| 3 x 5 |

- Now calculate 3 x 5.
Look for the answer
and colour the box.
- Continue until you
colour

| 8 |
|----|
| 9 x 6 |

| 8 | 36 | 32 | 24 | 50 | 15 |
|---|----|----|----|----|----|
| 9 x 6 | 5 x 7 | 7 x 7 | 3 x 4 | 6 x 5 | 2 x 9 |
| 81 | 9 | 7 | 60 | 64 | 14 |
| 4 x 7 | 5 x 10 | 9 x 1 | 3 x 7 | 3 x 9 | 5 x 9 |
| 21 | 16 | 40 | 20 | 54 | 12 |
| 8 x 6 | 7 x 8 | 6 x 10 | 7 x 2 | 3 x 5 | 2 x 8 |
| 27 | 63 | 45 | 56 | 80 | 18 |
| 10 x 8 | 8 x 8 | 9 x 9 | 8 x 1 | 1 x 7 | 6 x 6 |
| 72 | 28 | 35 | 49 | 30 | 48 |
| 8 x 4 | 6 x 4 | 9 x 8 | 4 x 10 | 7 x 9 | 4 x 5 |

**(b)** What do you notice about the pattern of the coloured boxes?
*It reads SH for Superhero.*

**2** Complete each pattern.

| 9 | x | 8 | = | 72 | | 9 | x | 1 | = | 9 |
|---|---|---|---|----|---|---|---|---|---|---|
| 8 | x | 7 | = | 56 | | 8 | x | 2 | = | 16 |
| 7 | x | 6 | = | 42 | | 7 | x | 3 | = | 21 |
| 6 | x | 5 | = | 30 | | 6 | x | 4 | = | 24 |
| 5 | x | 4 | = | 20 | | 5 | x | 5 | = | 25 |

**3** Multiply to find the missing numbers.

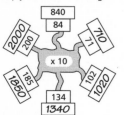

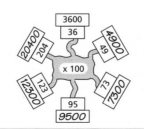

---

**1** Superhero and Mog take food and water
to the emergency area.
They give each person
- 4 *l* of milk
- 7 kg of vita-bics
- 6 kg of dried soup
- 5 kg of rice
- 9 *l* of water.

How much of each item did Superhero and Mog give?

| milk | vita-bics | dried soup | rice | water |
|------|-----------|------------|------|-------|
| 1386 | 1386 | 1386 | 1386 | 1386 |
| x 4 | x 7 | x 6 | x 5 | x 9 |
| 5544 | 9702 | 8316 | 6930 | 12474 |

**2** **(a)** 3215   **(b)** 743   **(c)** 3605   **(d)** 2089   **(e)** 863

| (a) | (b) | (c) | (d) | (e) |
|-----|-----|-----|-----|-----|
| 3215 | 743 | 3605 | 2089 | 863 |
| x 2 | x 8 | x 3 | x 7 | x 9 |
| 6430 | 5944 | 10815 | 14623 | 7767 |

**1** **(a)** £6456      **(b)** £16 240
    **(c)** £12 618      **(b)** £13 065

**2** £33 000

**3** **(a)** £11 376      **(b)** £14 966      **(c)** £16 375

**1** **(a)** £95·85      **(b)** £190·14      **(c)** £205·84
    **(d)** £87·44

**2** **(a)** £73·00      **(b)** £177·45      **(c)** £98·90
    **(d)** £275·10

**3** 3 lions and 2 Peter Pans

**1** **(a)** 6 sets with 1 eyepatch left over
    **(b)** 9 sets with 2 tubes left over
    **(c)** 6 sets with 1 bottle left over
    **(d)** 6 sets with 4 bandages left over

**2** **(a)** 8 r2    **(b)** 9 r1    **(c)** 7 r3    **(d)** 3 r3
    **(e)** 5 r2    **(f)** 6 r1    **(g)** 8    **(h)** 8

**3** 15     5     3     1

**4** **(a)** 1, 2, 7, 14      **(b)** 1, 2, 4, 5, 10, 20

## 14

**1** **(a)** 364 bottles with 1 bottle left over
**(b)** 98 tubes with 1 tube left over

**2** **(a)** 217 r1  **(b)** 89  **(c)** 163 r2

**3** **(a)** 704 strips with 3 pills left over
**(b)** 1067 strips with 2 pills left over

**4** 2055 and 3270

## 15

**1** **(a)** 8 bags with 3 rubies left over
**(b)** 9 bags with 2 opals left over

**2** **(a)** 5 r3  **(b)** 4 r3  **(c)** 5 r5  **(d)** 6 r1
**(e)** 7 r4  **(f)** 8 r4  **(g)** 9  **(h)** 6

**3** **(a)** 49 and 56  **(b)** 32 and 56

**4** **(a)** 382 r7  **(b)** 560  **(c)** 70 r8  **(d)** 406

## 16

**1** **(a)** 43 Dazzlers (and 2 rubies left over)
**(b)** 193 Dazzlers (and 3 rubies left over)
**(c)** 705 Dazzlers (and 5 rubies left over)

**2** **(a)** 182 Sparklers (and 3 diamonds left over)
**(b)** 405 Sparklers (and 4 diamonds left over)
**(c)** 706 Sparklers

**3** **(a)** 215 Starlights (and 1 sapphire left over)
**(b)** 377 Starlights (and 4 sapphires left over)
**(c)** 938 Starlights (and 7 sapphires left over)

**4** **(a)** 359 r5  **(b)** 152  **(c)** 870 r4  **(d)** 764

## 17

|  ¹3  |    |    |  ²6  |    |
|------|----|-----|-----|-----|
|  4   |    | ³2  |  8  |  8  |
| ⁴1   | 1  | 3   |  7  |     |
|  7   |    | 6   |     |     |
|      |    | ⁵2  |  9  | 0  | 4 |

## 18

**1** CAT FISH

**2** **(a)** answer wrong  **(b)** answer correct
**(c)** answer wrong

**3** 5712

## 19

**1** 21 boats

**2** 43 stacks

**3** 89 boxes

**4** 18 trips

---

Heinemann Mathematics 6   Home Link-up   |   Fractions: equivalence   **20**
Textbook pages 31 and 32

**1** Write equal fractions for each pair of designs.

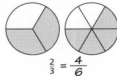

$\frac{2}{3} = \frac{4}{6}$      $\frac{3}{5} = \frac{12}{20}$

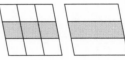
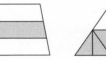

$\frac{3}{9} = \frac{1}{3}$      $\frac{6}{8} = \frac{3}{4}$

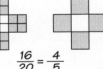

$\frac{1}{2} = \frac{5}{10}$      $\frac{16}{20} = \frac{4}{5}$

**2** Complete.  $\frac{1}{2} = \frac{3}{6}$      $\frac{4}{5} = \frac{8}{10}$      $\frac{2}{3} = \frac{8}{12}$

**3** Complete.  $\frac{6}{9} = \frac{2}{3}$      $\frac{15}{20} = \frac{3}{4}$      $\frac{30}{100} = \frac{3}{10}$

**4** Change  **(a)** $\frac{3}{5}$ to twentieths  **(b)** $\frac{9}{12}$ to quarters  **(c)** $\frac{1}{2}$ to hundredths

$\frac{12}{20}$      $\frac{3}{4}$      $\frac{50}{100}$

**5** Simplify.  $\frac{6}{8} = \frac{3}{4}$      $\frac{4}{10} = \frac{2}{5}$      $\frac{80}{100} = \frac{4}{5}$

## 21

**1** (a) $\frac{5}{10}$ or $\frac{1}{2}$ (b) $\frac{1}{10}$

**2** (a) $\frac{2}{20}$ or $\frac{1}{10}$ (b) $\frac{3}{20}$ (c) $\frac{5}{20}$ or $\frac{1}{4}$ (d) $\frac{10}{20}$ or $\frac{1}{2}$

**3** (a) $\frac{10}{100}$ or $\frac{1}{10}$ (b) $\frac{20}{100}$ or $\frac{1}{5}$ (c) $\frac{70}{100}$ or $\frac{7}{10}$

## 22

**1** (a) 8 (b) 9 (c) 7 (d) 10
(e) 6 (f) 6 (g) 9 (h) 8

**2** (a) 70 are oak (b) 35 are elm
(c) 28 are beech (d) 14 are ash

**3** (a) 243 (b) 236 (c) 59 (d) 58
(e) 47 (f) 25 (g) 43 (h) 51

---

| Heinemann Mathematics 6   Home Link-up<br>Textbook page 36 | Decimals: first decimal place, notation | **23**  |
|---|---|---|

**1** Colour to match.

( 43 tenths ) ( **5·1** ) ( 9 tenths ) ( 12·6 ) ( 3·0 ) ( **5 units and 1 tenth** )

( 30 tenths ) ( 4 units and 3 tenths ) ( **0·9** ) ( three units and no tenths )

( twelve and six tenths ) ( 4·3 ) ( **51 tenths** ) ( no units and nine tenths )

**2** Write in decimal form.

(a) two units and five tenths  _2·5_

(b) eleven and three tenths  _11·3_

(c) forty and one tenth  _40·1_

(d) twenty-six and nine tenths  _26·9_

**3** Arrange in order, starting with the smallest.

14·5  15·4  13·4  14·3  15·0  _13·4  14·3  14·5  15·0  15·4_

---

Possible answers are

## 24

**1** (a) 14·3 kg (b) 21·8 kg (c) 36·1 kg

**2** (a) 3·5 (b) 3·6 (c) 7·7 (d) 5·9
(e) 10·4

**3** (a) 11·3 (b) 53·0 (c) 47·9

**4** 7·7 kg of prawns are left.

**5** 30·9 kg

## 25

**1** (a) 2·4 kg (b) 7·2 kg (c) 3·0 kg

**2** (a) 30·6 (b) 32·5 (c) 19·6

**3** (a) 37 (b) 13·8 (c) correct answer
(d) 9·5 (e) 20 (f) correct answer

**4** (a) 6·9 kg (b) 14·2 kg (c) 16·3 kg (d) 10·5 kg
(e) 14·3 kg

---

| Heinemann Mathematics 6   Home Link-up<br>Textbook page 42, Workbook page 10 | Decimals: second decimal place, notation | **26**  |
|---|---|---|

This sign has 100 squares.
The fraction of the sign lit is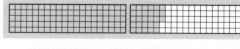

57 hundredths or $\frac{57}{100}$ or 0·57

**1** Write each of these fractions in two other ways:

(a) 42 hundredths  $\frac{42}{100}$  _0.42_ (b) $\frac{34}{100}$  _34 hundredths_  _0.34_

(c) 30 hundredths  $\frac{30}{100}$  _0.30_ (d) 0·47  _47 hundredths_  $\frac{47}{100}$

(e) 7 hundredths  $\frac{7}{100}$  _0.07_ (f) 0·09  _9 hundredths_  $\frac{9}{100}$

**2** Write these decimals in order, starting with the smallest.
0·32, 0·02, 0·23, 0·30, 0·22, 0·33
_0.02   0.22   0.23   0.30   0.32   0.33_

**3** (a) Colour to
show 1·28

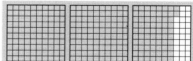

(b) Colour to
show 2·72

**4** Write in decimal form:

(a) 5 units and 11 hundredths  _5·11_ (b) 3 units and 62 hundredths  _3·62_

(c) 4 units and 70 hundredths  _4·70_ (d) 5 units and 4 hundredths  _5·04_

**5** Use the digits [1] [4] [9] and a decimal point each time.

Write as many different decimals as you can between 2 and 20.

_4·19    4·91    9·14    9·41    14·9    19·4_

## 27

**1** **(a)** 0·38  **(b)** 0·69  **(c)** 0·75  **(d)** 0·03

**2** **(a)** 3 tenths and 5 hundredths
**(b)** 5 tenths and 6 hundredths
**(c)** 2 tenths and 7 hundredths
**(d)** 4 tenths and 0 hundredths
**(e)** 0 tenths and 1 hundredth

**3** **(a)** 0·42 = 4 tenths and 2 hundredths = 0·4 + 0·02
**(b)** 0·21 = 2 tenths and 1 hundredth = 0·2 + 0·01
**(c)** 0·96 = 9 tenths and 6 hundredths = 0·9 + 0·06

**4** **(a)** 5 hundredths  **(b)** 5 units
**(c)** 5 tens  **(d)** 5 tenths

**5** 3·43, 4·03

## 28

**1** **(a)** 0·78  **(b)** 1·02  **(c)** 4·12
**(d)** 8·4  **(e)** 25·26  **(f)** 58·23

**2** carrot and cream  £1·56
lemon and cream  £1·58
chocolate and cream  £1·62
apple and cream  £1·43

**3** **(a)** £3·38  **(b)** £2·77

## 29

**1** **(a)** 5·17  **(b)** 10·36  **(c)** 9·76  **(d)** 29·87
**(e)** 5·65  **(f)** 18·96  **(g)** 30·33

**2** **(a)** 0·40 metres shorter  **(b)** £6·25

**3** **(a)** 1·27 metres longer  **(b)** £34·50

## 30

**1** 6·15 metres

**2** **(a)** 12·04 metres
**(b)** Bill's car and trailer are longer by 1·10 metres.

**3** **(a)** 25·2  **(b)** 28·8  **(c)** 6·7  **(d)** 5·9

**4** **(a)** 1·7 kg  **(b)** 17·6 kg  **(c)** 4·4 kg

## 31

**1** **(a)** • highest – Point C  • lowest – Point E
**(b)** 3·62 metres
**(c)** 17 m to the nearest metre.

**2** The steps reach the top of the cliffs at Point A because 109 x 0·17 m = 18·53 m.

**3** **(a)** The calculation will depend on child's choice of starting number.
**(b)** The finish number is always 10 times the starting number.

Extra

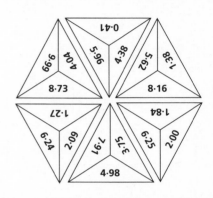

Each floor design has 100 tiles.

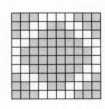

**1** Complete.

shaded → $\frac{28}{100}$ or **28** %  shaded → $\frac{64}{100}$ or **64** %

not shaded → $\frac{72}{100}$ or **72** %  not shaded → $\frac{36}{100}$ or **36** %

**2** **(a)** Complete:  5% = $\frac{5}{100}$  20% = $\frac{20}{100}$  30% = $\frac{30}{100}$  40% = $\frac{40}{100}$

**(b)** Colour:
5% red, 20% blue, 30% green and 40% yellow

*Other ways of colouring are possible.*

**(c)** What percentage is not coloured?  **5%**

**3** **(a)** Use red, blue and green to colour your own design.

**(b)** Complete.

_____ % is coloured red

_____ % is coloured blue

_____ % is coloured green

*Answers depend on the children's choice of colouring.*

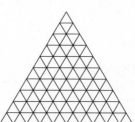

## 33

**1** $10\% = \frac{1}{10}$   $50\% = \frac{1}{2}$   $25\% = \frac{1}{4}$

**2** **(a)** 3   **(b)** 3   **(c)** 2   **(d)** 9
**(e)** 50   **(f)** 5

**3** **(a)** 10% of 80 is more   **(b)** 50% of 18 is more

**4** **(a)** 60 choose pheasant, 120 choose venison, 24 choose trout
**(b)** 15% choose salad

Heinemann Mathematics 6   Home Link-up
Workbook page 15

Pattern: function machines

## 34

Complete each function machine.

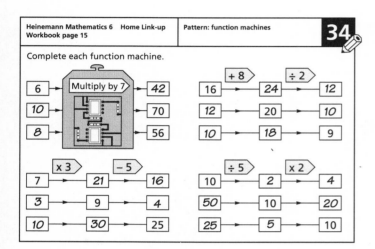

Heinemann Mathematics 6   Home Link-up
Workbook page 16, Textbook page 56

Pattern: word formulae

## 35

**1** **(a)** Draw the next two matchstick flag patterns.

**(b)** Complete.

| Number of flags | Number of matches |
|---|---|
| 1 | 5 |
| 2 | 10 |
| 3 | 15 |
| 4 | 20 |
| 5 | 25 |

**(c)** How many matches are needed for
- 8 flags ___40___
- 10 flags ___50___
- 20 flags? ___100___

**(d)** Complete.
The number of matches is ___5___ times the number of flags.

**2** **(a)** Complete.

| Number of shields | Number of swords |
|---|---|
| 1 | 2 |
| 2 | 3 |
| 3 | 4 |
| 4 | 5 |
| 5 | 6 |

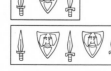
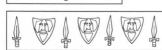

**(b)** How many swords are needed for • 7 shields ___8___ • 10 shields ___11___ ?
The number of swords is _one more than the number of shields._

## 36

**1** **(a)** 555 passengers   **(b)** 666 passengers

**2** **(a)** 784 passengers   **(b)** 952 passengers

**3** (a) is cheaper by £5 (£798-£793)

## 37

**1** **(a)** £1128   **(b)** 600 watches

**2** **(a)** £1368   **(b)** 2124 necklaces

**3** **(a)** £3420   **(b)** £3135

## 38

**1** **(a)**
```
19 | 67
19 | 1
   48
19 | 1
   29
19 | 1
   10 | 3
```
Answer: 3r10

**(b)**
```
57 | 171
57 | 1
  114
57 | 1
   57
57 | 1
    0 | 3
```
Answer: 3

**(c)**
```
85 | 173
85 | 1
   88
85 | 1
    3 | 2
```
Answer: 2r3

**2** **(a)** 3 sandwiches each and 2 left over
**(b)** 2 sandwiches each and 19 left over

## 39

**1** **(a)** 12r5   **(b)** 13   **(c)** 30r10

**2** **(a)** 22 groups   **(b)** 15 passengers are left

**3** **(a)** 12 passports **(b)** 1 passport

---

### Extra

Use a calculator.

**1** Complete.   **(a)** 21 × 24 = ___504___   **(b)** 13 × 62 = ___806___
12 × 42 = ___504___   31 × 26 = ___806___

**2** There are other sets of numbers like this.
Find the missing digit and the product for each of these.

**(a)** 12 × 6 $\boxed{3}$ = ___756___   **(b)** 23 × 9 $\boxed{6}$ = ___2208___
21 × $\boxed{3}$ 6 = ___756___   32 × $\boxed{6}$ 9 = ___2208___

## 40

**1** 4 m 45 cm

**2** 1 m 55 cm

**3** (a) 7 m 75 cm  (b) 9 m  (c) 8 m 80 cm

**4** (a) 20 m  (b) 3 m  (c) 9 m 60 cm
(d) 8 m 16 cm

## 41

**1** (a) 40 cm  (b) 1 m 20 cm  (c) 1 m 60 cm
(d) 1 m

**2** (a) 7 m
(b) Shelter A is 9 m high, shelter B is 8 m high
and shelter C is 5 m 60 cm high. The giraffe
could stand upright in shelters A and B.

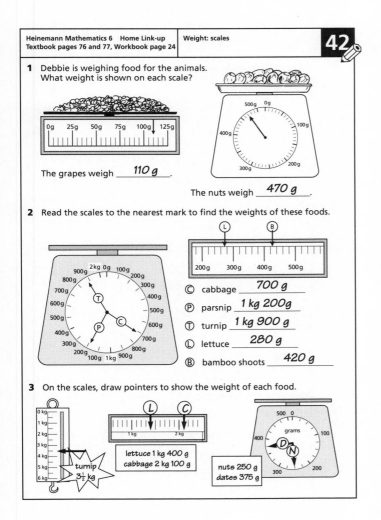

**1** Debbie is weighing food for the animals.
What weight is shown on each scale?

The grapes weigh ___110 g___.

The nuts weigh ___470 g___.

**2** Read the scales to the nearest mark to find the weights of these foods.

© cabbage ___700 g___
℗ parsnip ___1 kg 200g___
Ⓣ turnip ___1 kg 900 g___
Ⓛ lettuce ___280 g___
Ⓑ bamboo shoots ___420 g___

**3** On the scales, draw pointers to show the weight of each food.

lettuce 1 kg 400 g
cabbage 2 kg 100 g

turnip 3½ kg

nuts 250 g
dates 375 g

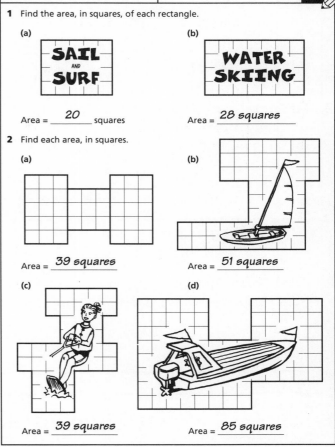

**1** Find the area, in squares, of each rectangle.

(a) SAIL AND SURF

Area = ___20___ squares

(b) WATER SKIING

Area = ___28 squares___

**2** Find each area, in squares.

(a)

Area = ___39 squares___

(b)

Area = ___51 squares___

(c)

Area = ___39 squares___

(d)

Area = ___85 squares___

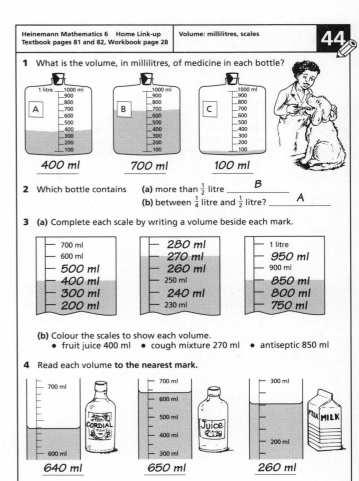

**1** What is the volume, in millilitres, of medicine in each bottle?

A ___400 ml___  B ___700 ml___  C ___100 ml___

**2** Which bottle contains  (a) more than ½ litre ___B___
(b) between ¼ litre and ½ litre? ___A___

**3** (a) Complete each scale by writing a volume beside each mark.

700 ml
600 ml
500 ml
400 ml
300 ml
200 ml

280 ml
270 ml
260 ml
250 ml
240 ml
230 ml

1 litre
950 ml
900 ml
850 ml
800 ml
750 ml

(b) Colour the scales to show each volume.
• fruit juice 400 ml  • cough mixture 270 ml  • antiseptic 850 ml

**4** Read each volume **to the nearest mark**.

700 ml
600 ml
CORDIAL

640 ml

700 ml
600 ml
500 ml
400 ml
300 ml
Juice

650 ml

300 ml
200 ml
MILK

260 ml

## 45

**1**  
| A | – 35 minutes | B | – 1 hour 5 minutes |
| C | – 45 minutes | D | – 1 hour 20 minutes |

**2** (a) 3.30 pm  (b) 3 hours 45 minutes

**3** (a) Freda Star – 2 hours 50 minutes  
Clint Logan – 3 hours 5 minutes  
(b) 30 minutes (from 11.20 am to 12.10 pm)

## 46

**1** (a) 1.30 pm  (b) 3.00 pm  (c) 5.20 pm

**2** *After Dark* – 8.45 pm  *Nightmare* – 5.45 pm  
*Gold Fever* – 11.15 am  *Blanche* – 00.30 am

## 47

**1** (a) 1.45 pm  (b) 11.15 pm  (c) 3.35 pm  
(d) 8.05 pm

**2** Studio 1 – 10.10 am  Studio 2 – 10.35 am  
Studio 3 – 11.20 am

**3** 10.55 am

## 48

**1** (a) 06.15  (b) 18.00  (c) 13.05  (d) 23.00  
(e) 05.50

**2** (a) 2.00 pm  (b) 1.00 am  (c) 5.45 pm  
(d) 9.10 am  (e) 12.00 noon

**3**  
| 11.45 | Cartoon Time |
| 12.15 | Travelscene |
| 13.05 | Lunchdate |
| 15.10 | Film on 6 |
| 16.50 | News |
| 17.00 | Weather |
| 17.03 | Quickquiz |
| 17.35 | Cooking for Two |

**4** (a) *Cartoon Time*  (b) *Lunchdate*  
(c) *News*

**5** (a) 15.10  (b) 17.35

---

**1** Use the notices. Complete the schedule for Tuesday afternoon.

| Tuesday afternoon programmes 6TV | |
| --- | --- |
| Red Dragon | 11.59 |
| News | 13.00 |
| Aerobics | 13.25 |
| Sportsquiz | 13.55 |
| Art Facts | 14.28 |
| Hospital Soap | 15.15 |
| Buzzword | 16.07 |
| Popview | 16.40 |
| Dungeon | 17.10 |

**2** Name the programme which starts at  
16.40 _Popview_  15.15 _Hospital Soap_

**3** Which programme is showing at  
13.20 _News_  14.00? _Sportsquiz_

**4** Which programme starts  
just before 2.30 pm  just after 4.05 pm?  
_Art Facts_  _Buzzword_

**5** There was picture interference for one hour, starting at 13.35.  
(a) When did the interference end? _14.35_   
(b) Which programmes were affected?  
_Aerobics, Sportsquiz, Art Facts_

*Problem solving*

---

Complete Antonia's schedule for these programmes.

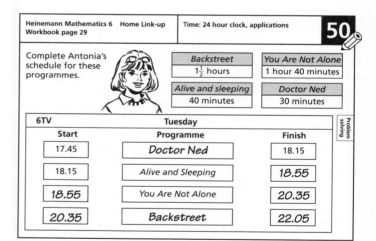

| Backstreet | You Are Not Alone |
| --- | --- |
| 1½ hours | 1 hour 40 minutes |

| Alive and sleeping | Doctor Ned |
| --- | --- |
| 40 minutes | 30 minutes |

| 6TV | Tuesday | |
| --- | --- | --- |
| **Start** | **Programme** | **Finish** |
| 17.45 | Doctor Ned | 18.15 |
| 18.15 | Alive and Sleeping | 18.55 |
| 18.55 | You Are Not Alone | 20.35 |
| 20.35 | Backstreet | 22.05 |

*Problem solving*

---

**Extra**   Ann and Shareen left at the same time (15.45). The other presenters left at these times:  
Tracey – 14.55  Bill – 15.15  
Desmond – 15.40

**1** Write the co-ordinates of each Star Freighter shown on the computer screen.

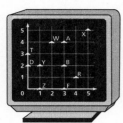

**Star Freighters' Co-ordinates**

A ( _3_ , _4_ )   B _(3,2)_
D _(0,2)_   F _(3,0)_
R _(4,1)_   T _(0,3)_
W _(2,4)_   X _(5,5)_
Y _(1,2)_   Z _(1,0)_

**2** Mark these points on the grid below. Join them, **in order**, with straight lines, to make a picture of a Star Freighter.

Star Freighter X:  (5,4)  (7,5)  (9,5)  (9,4)  (13,4)  (18,6)  (17,3)  (18,2)
(15,1)  (10,1)  (5,0)  (5,1)  (0,3)  (3,4) and back to (5,4)

**3** **(a)** Mark these points. Join them, in order, to make half of a symmetrical picture.
(1,3)  (1,4)  (2,5)  (4,3)  (5,4)
(6,3)  (8,5)  (9,4)  (9,3)
**(b)** Draw the other half and list the co-ordinates in order.

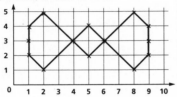

_(1,3) (1,2) (2,1) (4,3) (5,2)_
_(6,3) (8,1) (9,2) (9,3)_

---

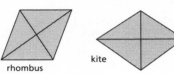

square        rhombus        kite

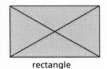

rectangle        parallelogram

**1** Which shapes have
- no lines of symmetry _____ *parallelogram*
- only one line of symmetry _____ *kite*
- only two lines of symmetry _____ *rhombus rectangle*
- four lines of symmetry? _____ *square*

**2** Draw the diagonals on each shape.

**3** Which shapes have a diagonal which is also a line of symmetry?
*kite  rhombus  square*

**4** Cut out this kite. Cut along its longer diagonal. Use the pieces to make a shape which has no lines of symmetry. Stick the shape below.

*Various answers are possible.*

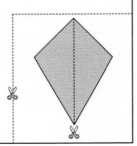

---

**You need the six-piece tangram.** Make each shape.
Draw round the pieces to show how you did this.

---

**1** Trace each shape and mark one corner.
Find how often the shape fits its outline in one full turn.

*three ways*        *two ways*

*one way*        *6 ways*

**2** Trace each design and shade it as shown.
Find how often the shaded design fits in one full turn.

*two ways*        *3 ways*        *two ways*

**3** Colour this shape so that the coloured design fits its outline
- in two ways   - in three ways.

*Other ways of colouring are possible.*

Problem solving

**1**

There are two sheets for this activity.

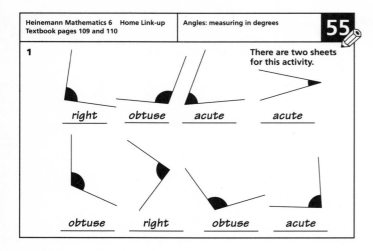

right     obtuse     acute     acute

obtuse     right     obtuse     acute

---

**55**   continued

**2**

| Angle A | acute | 70° |
|---------|-------|-----|
| Angle B | acute | 55° |
| Angle C | acute | 25° |
| Angle D | obtuse | 125° |
| Angle E | acute | 65° |
| Angle F | obtuse | 110° |

**3** (a) Angle C and angle E
    (b) Angle B and angle D
        Angle A and angle F

---

Class 6 buys some of Topperton Garden Centre's heathers.

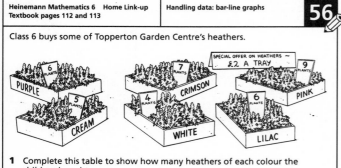

**1** Complete this table to show how many heathers of each colour the children bought.

| Heather colour | white | cream | pink | lilac | purple | crimson |
|----------------|-------|-------|------|-------|--------|---------|
| Number of trays | 9 | 8 | 8 | 9 | 8 | 10 |
| Number in 1 tray | 4 | 5 | 9 | 6 | 6 | 7 |
| Total number of plants | 36 | 40 | 72 | 54 | 48 | 70 |

**2** Complete the bar-line graph to show the number of heathers bought by Class 6.

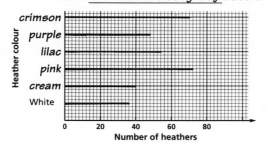

*Number of heathers bought by Class 6*

**3** Write a question about your graph for a friend to answer.
*Dependent on answers given by children.*

---

**57**

**1** (a) July     (b) December

**2** (a) 4 days    (b) 3 days

**3** (a) April, October
    (b) June, July, August, September

**4** The number of sunny days increases until the middle of summer and then decreases.

---

These measurements were taken by children in Class 6.

| How far we can jump, in centimetres | | | | |
|---|---|---|---|---|
| Lyn – 142 | Richard – 151 | Sandra – 148 | Aziz – 143 | Sue – 148 |
| Kathryn – 142 | Abdul – 152 | Alan – 153 | Sam – 150 | Patricia – 151 |
| Sarah – 148 | Iona – 153 | John – 156 | | |

**1** Complete: The distances jumped range from __142 cm__ to __156 cm__.

**2** Write the distances jumped, in order, starting with the shortest.
_142_, _142_, _143_, _148_, _148_, _148_, _150_, _151_, _151_, _152_, _153_, _153_, _156_

**3** What distance is ● the mode __148 cm__ ● the median? __150 cm__

**4** Calculate the mean distance jumped. __149 cm__

---

**1** Carry out a survey to find which is the most common car colour. Complete this table for the **first 50** cars you see.

| Colour | Tally marks | Total |
|--------|-------------|-------|
| black | | |
| white | | |
| red | | |
| blue | | |
| green | | |
| other | | |
| **Total** | | **50** |

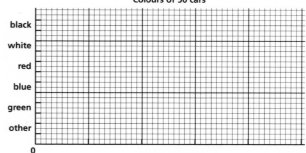

*Answers to this page depend on the information collected by the children.*

**2** Use your data to complete this bar graph.

Colours of 50 cars

black
white
red
blue
green
other

0     **Number of cars**

**3** At school, look at the graphs drawn by the others in your group. Write about what you notice.

The table shows the possible ways of choosing **two of the white shapes.**

| cube | 2 | 1 |
|---|---|---|
| sphere | 0 | 1 |

**1** Complete the table to show all the possible ways of choosing **two of the grey shapes.**

| cuboid | 2 | 1 | 1 | 0 | 0 | 0 |
|---|---|---|---|---|---|---|
| cylinder | 0 | 1 | 0 | 2 | 1 | 0 |
| cone | 0 | 0 | 1 | 0 | 1 | 2 |

**2** Complete this table to show all the possible ways of choosing **one white shape and one grey shape.**

| cube | 1 | 1 | 1 | 0 | 0 | 0 |
|---|---|---|---|---|---|---|
| sphere | 0 | 0 | 0 | 1 | 1 | 1 |
| cuboid | 1 | 0 | 0 | 1 | 0 | 0 |
| cylinder | 0 | 1 | 0 | 0 | 1 | 0 |
| cone | 0 | 0 | 1 | 0 | 0 | 1 |